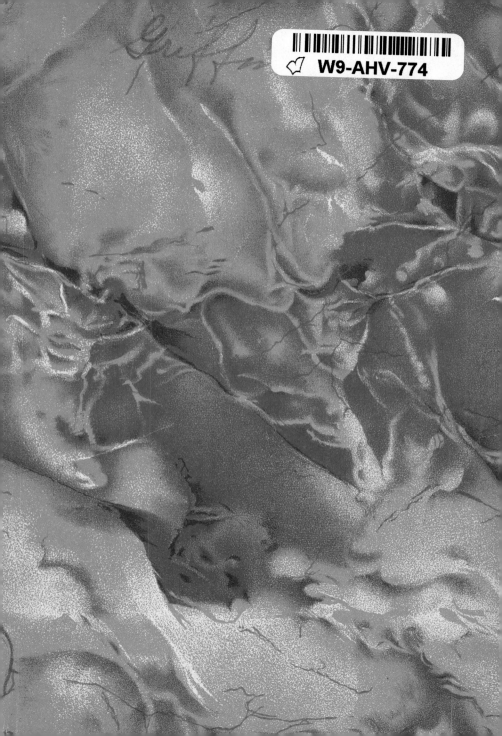

RODEHEAVER'S

Gospel Solos
and Duets

No. 2

Compiled by
Y. P. RODEHEAVER

A Collection of
SPECIAL GOSPEL SONGS
for Special Singers

PRICE, $1.00 NET

Published by
The RODEHEAVER
HALL — MACK Co.
28 East Jackson Boulevard   124 North Fifteenth Street
CHICAGO   PHILADELPHIA
Printed in U. S. A.

Suggestions

* * *

Our first collection of special gospel solos and duets met with such kindly reception that we have been persuaded, with the suggestions and assistance of many of our friends, to issue another collection.

It has been quite a task, and the book has been delayed much longer than we expected, in trying to find satisfactory material, but we bring it forth now, and we hope you will be pleased with it, and find it a valuable help in your work.

Those who may not be accustomed to adapting songs for the different voices, in singing duets, will find a very pleasing part for the tenor, in many selections, by singing the alto an octave higher. See Nos. 66, 74, 75 and 166.

You will note that in a few of the songs the melody is found in the alto, and these songs will make very satisfactory solos for alto or baritone. We will refer especially to Nos. 71, 85, 91, 93, 115, 148 and 173.

You will also find the melody in the tenor of several of the numbers, which can be used as solos for soprano, tenor, or baritone, as in Nos. 7, 13 and 88.

We are very grateful to our many friends for the valuable help and suggestions they have given us, without which we would not have been successful in securing a number of these splendid songs.

THE PUBLISHERS.

WONDERFUL MORNING

A. H. A.

Rev. A. H. Ackley

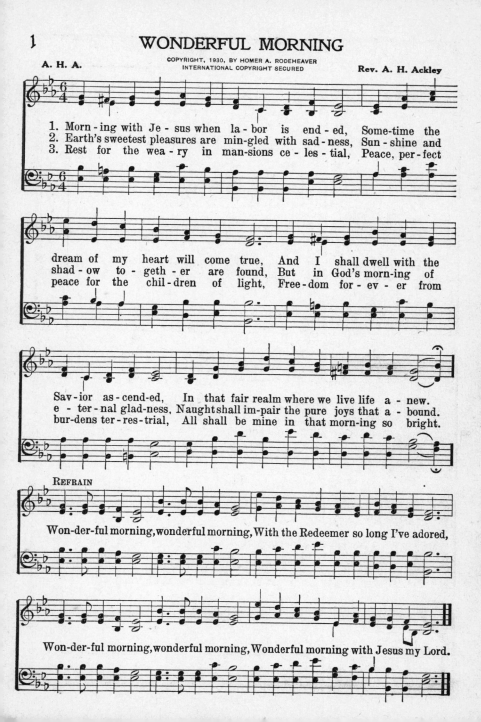

1. Morn-ing with Je-sus when la-bor is end-ed, Some-time the
2. Earth's sweetest pleasures are min-gled with sad-ness, Sun-shine and
3. Rest for the wea-ry in man-sions ce-les-tial, Peace, per-fect

dream of my heart will come true, And I shall dwell with the
shad-ow to-geth-er are found, But in God's morn-ing of
peace for the chil-dren of light, Free-dom for-ev-er from

Sav-ior as-cend-ed, In that fair realm where we live life a-new.
e-ter-nal glad-ness, Naught shall im-pair the pure joys that a-bound.
bur-dens ter-res-trial, All shall be mine in that morn-ing so bright.

REFRAIN

Won-der-ful morning, wonderful morning, With the Redeemer so long I've adored,

Won-der-ful morning, wonderful morning, Wonderful morning with Jesus my Lord.

THE OLD RUGGED CROSS

REV. GEO. BENNARD   REV. GEO. BENNARD

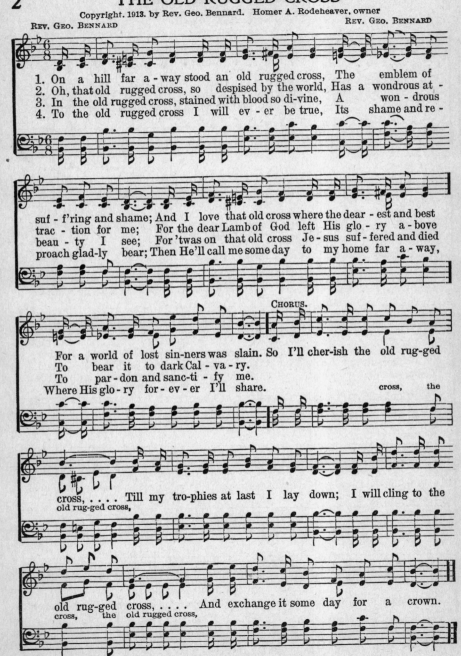

1. On a hill far a-way stood an old rugged cross, The emblem of
2. Oh, that old rugged cross, so despised by the world, Has a wondrous at -
3. In the old rugged cross, stained with blood so di-vine, A won - drous
4. To the old rugged cross I will ev - er be true, Its shame and re -

suf-f'ring and shame; And I love that old cross where the dear - est and best
trac - tion for me; For the dear Lamb of God left His glo - ry a-bove
beau - ty I see; For 'twas on that old cross Je - sus suf - fered and died
proach glad-ly bear; Then He'll call me some day to my home far a - way,

CHORUS.

For a world of lost sin-ners was slain. So I'll cher-ish the old rug-ged
To bear it to dark Cal - va - ry.
To par-don and sanc-ti - fy me.
Where His glo - ry for - ev - er I'll share.   cross, the

cross, ... Till my tro-phies at last I lay down; I will cling to the
old rug-ged cross,

old rug-ged cross, ... And exchange it some day for a crown.
cross, the old rugged cross,

3

BESIDE BLUE GALILEE

SOLO AND CHORUS

C. H. G.

Chas. H. Gabriel.

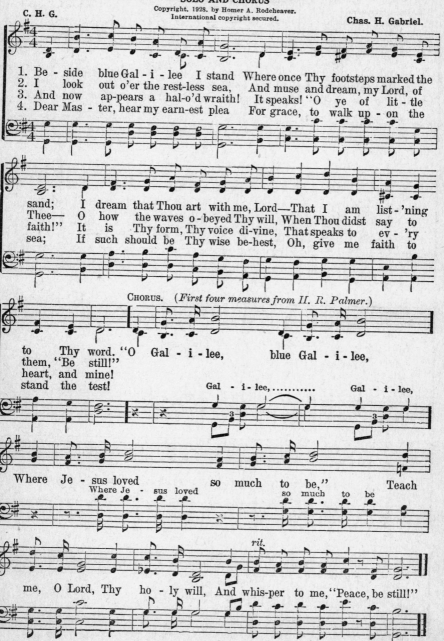

1. Be - side blue Gal - i - lee I stand Where once Thy footsteps marked the sand; I dream that Thou art with me, Lord—That I am list-'ning to to Thy word.
2. I look out o'er the rest-less sea, And muse and dream, my Lord, of Thee—O how the waves o-beyed Thy will, When Thou didst say to them, "Be still!"
3. And now ap-pears a hal-o'd wraith! It speaks! "O ye of lit - tle faith!" It is Thy form, Thy voice di-vine, That speaks to ev - 'ry heart, and mine!
4. Dear Mas - ter, hear my earn-est plea For grace, to walk up - on the sea; If such should be Thy wise be-hest, Oh, give me faith to stand the test!

CHORUS. (*First four measures from H. R. Palmer.*)

"O Gal - i - lee, blue Gal - i - lee, Gal - i - lee,.......... Gal - i - lee,

Where Je - sus loved so much to be," Teach

Where Je - sus loved so much to be

rit.

me, O Lord, Thy ho - ly will, And whis-per to me, "Peace, be still!"

4

OUT OF THE DEPTHS

Charles H. Gabriel

Charles H. Gabriel

DUET. *Tenor (or Soprano) and Alto*

1. Out of the depths did I cry un - to Thee, And in Thy love Thou didst
2. Day aft - er day more and more do I need Thy grace to keep me, Thy
3. Like as a fa - ther's Thy mer - cy is deep, For - ev - er pres - ent to

an - swer me;   Tri - al was changed in - to won - der - ful peace,
hand to lead;   I   am as noth - ing, till Thou wilt a - bide
save and keep. Love me, and guide me, and keep me, I   pray,

CHORUS

When from my sor - row I found re - lease.
Close by me ev - er my way to guide.   Out of the depths did I
Till I be - hold Thee in end - less day.

cry un - to Thee, And blessings di - vine were showered on me!   Out of the

gloom Thou hast shown me the way, Out of the night in - to glo - rious day.

5 PRECIOUS HIDING PLACE

(ALTO AND TENOR DUET)

Avis B. Christiansen

Wendell P. Loveless

1. I was straying when Christ found me In the night so dark and cold,
2. With His nail-scarred hand He bro't me To the shel-ter of His love;
3. Tho' the night be dark a-round me, I am safe, for He is near;

Ten-der-ly His arm went round me And He bore me to His fold.
Of His grace and will He taught me, And of heav'n-ly rest a-bove.
Nev-er shall my foes con-found me, While the Saviour's voice I hear.

CHORUS.

Pre-cious hid-ing place, Pre-cious hid-ing place, In the

shel-ter of His love; Not a doubt or fear, Since my

rit.

Lord is near, And I'm shel-tered in His love.

6 I SHALL BE SATISFIED THEN

James C. Moore   James C. Moore

1. When all my la-bors on earth have been done, Heaven's bright crown for e-
2. When all my tri-als and troub-les are o'er, Sad-ness and sor-row be
3. Won-der-ful joy, there my Sav-ior to meet, Bask in the light of His
4. There where all shadows are driv-en a-way, Where is no night, but the

ter-ni-ty won, 'Tis by the grace of the In-fi-nite One,
mine nev-er-more, Loved ones will greet me on heav-en's glad shore,
love so com-plete, Liv-ing for-e'er in such fel-low-ship sweet,
bright-est of day, With my dear Sav-ior and loved ones to stay,

CHORUS

I shall be sat-is-fied then. I shall be sat-is-fied then. . . . .
sat-is-fied then,

I shall be sat-is-fied then, ... Joy will be mine with
e-ven then,

love all di-vine, I shall be sat-is-fied then. . . . .
sat-is-fied then.

HE BORE THE CROSS FOR ME

Rev. W. C. Poole

B. D. Ackley

Duet. *Alto and Tenor*

1. Be-cause my Sav-ior from a-bove Came seek-ing me in match-less love,
2. Be-cause He walked in Gal-i-lee, And prayed in dark Geth-sem-a-ne,
3. Be-cause He left His heav'nly home And climbed up Cal-va-ry a-lone

And bore the cross that love to prove, I'll bear the cross for Him.
To save a world like you and me, I'll bear the cross for Him.
To save and make me all His own, I'll bear the cross for Him.

CHORUS

Be-cause He bore the cross for me, Be-cause He
Be-cause He Be-cause He

died on Cal-va-ry; I've heard His call,
I've heard His call, ... I owe my

I owe my all To Him who bore the cross for me.
all. . . . . .

8

A NAIL IN HIS HAND

E. E. Hewitt

B. D. Ackley

1. The spear and the thorn by the Sav-ior were borne, That we might wear
2. The taunt and the blow, with Geth-sem-a-ne's woe, Were suf-fered by
3. O let us be-lieve, life e-ter-nal re-ceive, And serve Him with

crowns of de-light; His gar-ments were red, with the blood that He shed,
Him for our sake; For grace so su-preme, guilt-y souls to re-deem,
joy in His name; O-bey-ing His call, let us yield Him our all,

CHORUS

That ours might be spot-less and white.
What of-f'ring of love shall we make? He bore a nail in His
His Gos-pel to oth-ers pro-claim.

hand for you, A nail in His hand for me; O, won-der-ful love, that

came from a-bove, To seek and to save you and me! . . . .
you and me!

9 BEYOND EARTH'S SORROWS

Gipsy Simon Smith

Geo. C. Stebbins

10 CAN THE WORLD SEE JESUS IN YOU?

Mrs. C. H. Morris   Mrs. C. H. Morris

1. Do we live so close to the Lord to-day, Pass-ing to and
2. Do we love, with love to His own a-kin, All His crea-tures
3. As an o-pen book they our lives will read, To our words and

fro on life's bus-y way, That the world in us can a like-ness see
lost in the mire of sin? Will we reach a hand, what-so-e'er it cost,
acts giv-ing dai-ly heed; Will they be at-tract-ed, or turn a-way

Chorus

To the Man of Cal-va-ry?
To re-claim a sin-ner lost?   Can the world see Je-sus in
From the Christ we love to-day?
    1. Man of Cal-va-ry?   Can the world see

me? Can the world see Je-sus in you?   Does your love to Him ring
Je-sus in me? Can the world see Je-sus in you?

true, and your life and service, too? Can the world see Je-sus in you?
                                                            me—in you?

BEAUTIFUL BECKONING HANDS

C. C. Luther   C. C. Luther

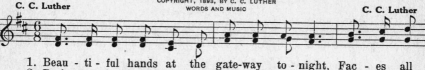

1. Beau - ti - ful hands at the gate-way to - night, Fac - es all
2. Beck - on - ing hands of a moth - er whose love Sac - ri - ficed
3. Beau - ti - ful hands of a lit - tle one, see! Ba - by voice
4. Beck - on - ing hands of a hus - band, a wife; Watch-ing and
5. Bright-est and best of that glo - ri - ous throng, Cen - ter of

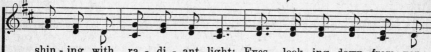

shin - ing with ra - di - ant light; Eyes look-ing down from yon
life her de - vo - tion to prove; Hands of a fa - ther to
call - ing, O moth - er, for thee; Ro - sy-cheeked dar - ling, the
wait - ing the loved one of life; Hands of a broth - er, a
all and the theme of their song, Je - sus, our Sav - ior, the

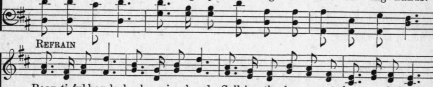

heav - en - ly home, Beau - ti - ful hands they are beck - on - ing "come."
mem - o - ry dear, Beck - on up high - er the wait - ing ones here.
light of the home, Tak - en so ear - ly, is beck - on - ing "come."
sis - ter, a friend, Out from the gate-way to - night they ex - tend.
pierc - ed one stands, Lov - ing - ly call - ing with beck - on - ing hands.

REFRAIN

Beau - ti - ful hands, beck - on - ing hands, Call-ing the dear ones to heav-en-ly lands;

Beau - ti - ful hands, beck - on - ing hands, Beau-ti-ful, beau-ti-ful beck-on-ing hands.

12 GOD'S TOMORROW.

A. H. A.

A. H. Ackley

1. God's tomorrow is a day of gladness, And its joys shall nev-er fade;
2. God's tomorrow is a day of greeting: We shall see the Savior's face;
3. God's tomorrow is a day of glo - ry: We shall wear the crown of life;

No more weeping, no more sense of sad-ness, No more foes to make a - fraid.
And our longing hearts a-wait the meeting In that ho - ly, hap-py place.
Sing thro' countless years love's old, old story, Free for-ev - er from all strife.

REFRAIN.

God's to - mor - row, God's to-mor - row, Ev - 'ry cloud will pass a-way

At the dawning of that day; God's to - mor - row, No more sor - row,

For I know that God's to - mor-row Will be bet - ter than to - day!

13 THE LOVE-LIGHTED CROSS

Rev. A. H. Ackley

B. D. Ackley

DUET

1. The love-light-ed cross nev-er los-es its glow, It shines thro' the dark-ness of sor-row and woe, God's in-fi-nite, ten-der com-pas-sion to show; I'll cling to the love-light-ed cross. . . .

2. The love-light-ed cross of-fers won-der-ful peace, For-give-ness for sin and the cap-tive's re-lease, A song of re-joic-ing that nev-er shall cease; I'll cling to the love-light-ed cross. . . .

3. The love-light-ed cross points the way to the sky, And tells of a home in the sweet by and by, Where we shall see Je-sus as-cend-ed on high; I'll cling to the love-light-ed cross. . . .

CHORUS

The bless-ed old cross, the Cal-va-ry cross, The love-light-ed cross of Je-sus; Thro' gain or thro' loss, I'll cling to the cross, The love-lighted cross of Je-sus.

WONDERFUL JESUS

(The Gipsy Smith Campaign Song)

14

Annie B. Russell

Ernest O. Sellers

1. There is nev-er a day so drear-y, There is nev-er a
2. There is nev-er a cross so heav-y, There is nev-er a
3. There is nev-er a care or bur-den, There is nev-er a
4. There is nev-er a guilt-y sin-ner, There is nev-er a

night so long, (so long,) But the soul that is trust-ing Je-sus Will
weight of woe, (of woe,) But that Je-sus will help to car-ry Be-
grief or loss, (or loss,) But that Je-sus in love will light-en When
wan-d'ring one, (not one,) But that God can in mer-cy par-don Thro'

CHORUS.

somewhere find a song. (a song.)
cause He lov-eth so. (loves so.) Won-der-ful, won-der-ful Je-sus,
car-ried to the cross. (the cross.)
Je-sus Christ, His Son. (His Son.)

In the heart He implanteth a song:.... A song of de-liv-'rance, of
He planteth a song:

cour-age, of strength, In the heart He im-plant-eth a song. (a song.)

15 JESUS KNOWS

Albert A. Rand

H. A Henry

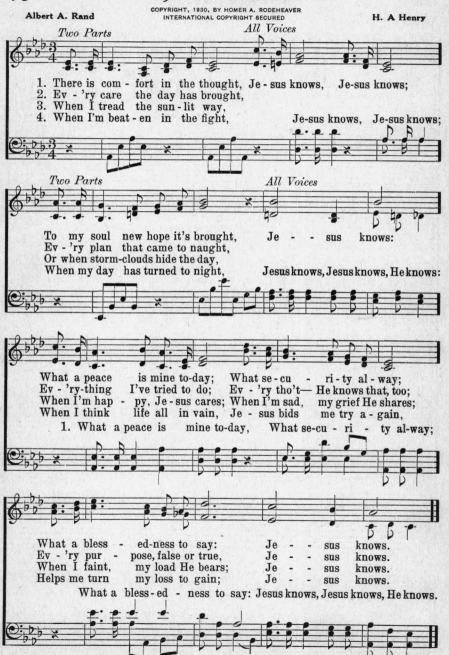

1. There is com - fort in the thought, Je - sus knows, Je-sus knows;
2. Ev - 'ry care the day has brought,
3. When I tread the sun - lit way,
4. When I'm beat - en in the fight,

Je-sus knows, Je-sus knows;

To my soul new hope it's brought, Je - - sus knows:
Ev - 'ry plan that came to naught,
Or when storm-clouds hide the day,
When my day has turned to night,

Jesus knows, Jesus knows, He knows:

What a peace is mine to-day; What se-cu - ri - ty al-way;
Ev - 'ry-thing I've tried to do; Ev - 'ry tho't— He knows that, too;
When I'm hap - py, Je-sus cares; When I'm sad, my grief He shares;
When I think life all in vain, Je - sus bids me try a - gain,

1. What a peace is mine to-day, What se-cu - ri - ty al-way;

What a bless - ed-ness to say: Je - - sus knows.
Ev - 'ry pur - pose, false or true, Je - - sus knows.
When I faint, my load He bears; Je - - sus knows.
Helps me turn my loss to gain; Je - - sus knows.

What a bless-ed - ness to say: Jesus knows, Jesus knows, He knows.

16

DEATH IS ONLY A DREAM

HYMN USED BY PER. THE R. M. McINTOSH CO., OWNER OF THE COPYRIGHT
STANDARD PUB. CO., OWNER

C. W. Ray   A. J. Buchanan

SOLO

1. Sad - ly we sing, and with trem - u - lous breath, As we stand by the
2. Why should we weep when the wea - ry ones rest In the bos - om of
3. Naught in the riv - er the saints should ap-pall, Tho' it fright-ful - ly
4. O - ver the tur - bid and on - rush - ing tide Doth the light of e-

mys - ti - cal stream, ... In the val - ley and by the dark
Je - sus su - preme, ... In the man-sions of glo - ry pre-
dis - mal may seem; .... In the arms of their Sav - ior no
ter - ni - ty gleam; .... And the ran-somed the dark - ness and

riv - er of death, And yet 'tis no more than a dream. ...
pared for the blest? For death is no more than a dream. ...
ill can be - fall, They find it no more than a dream. ...
storm shall out-ride, To wake with glad smiles from their dream. ...

CHORUS

On - ly a dream, on - ly a dream, And glo-ry be-yond the dark stream; How

DEATH IS ONLY A DREAM

peace-ful the slumber, how hap-py the waking, For death is on - ly a dream.

17 ERE YOU LEFT YOUR ROOM

Mary A. Kidder

W. O. Perkins

1. Ere you left your room this morn-ing, Did you think to pray? In the name of
2. When your heart was filled with an-ger, Did you think to pray? Did you plead for
3. When sore tri - als came up - on you, Did you think to pray? When your soul was

Christ, our Sav - ior, Did you sue for lov-ing fa - vor, As a shield to-day?
grace, my broth-er, That you might forgive an-oth - er Who had crossed your way?
full of sor - row, Balm of Gil-ead did you bor - row At the gates of day?

CHORUS

Oh, how pray-ing rests the wea - ry! Prayer will change the night to day;

So when life seems dark and drear - y, Don't for-get to pray.

NAILED TO THE CROSS

Mrs. Frank A. Breck

Crant Colfax Tullar

DUET *Ad lib.*

1. There was One who was will-ing to die in my stead, That a soul so un-
2. He is ten - der and lov - ing and pa-tient with me, While He cleans-es my
3. I will cling to my Sav-ior and nev - er de-part— I will joy-ful-ly

worth - y might live, And the path to the cross He was will - ing to tread,
heart of the dross, But "there's no con-dem-na-tion"—I know I am free,
jour - ney each day, With a song on my lips and a song in my heart,

REFRAIN

All the sins of my life to for - give.
For my sins are all nailed to the cross. They are nailed to the cross,
That my sins have been tak - en a - way.

pp

They are nailed to the cross, O how much He was will-ing to bear! With what

rit.

an-guish and loss Je-sus went to the cross! But He carried my sins with Him there.

FAR AWAY

Fanny J. Crosby

B. D. Ackley

DUET. *Tenor (or Soprano) and Alto*

1. Where is now the hap-py cir - cle, Gathered 'round the lin-den tree,
2. Some in fields of dis - tant la - bor Toil, the light of truth to spread,
3. Thus with years of con-stant chang-es, Joys and sor - rows come and go,

In the gloam-ing of the twi - light Sing-ing songs of mer - ry glee?
Some in hum-bler sta-tions walk-ing, Rug-ged steeps with pa-tience tread;
Like the ev - er - roll - ing sea - sons, Like the tides that ebb and flow;

Gone, the brook - let soft - ly mur-murs; Gone, the zeph - yrs gen - tly say;
Oth - ers from their cares are rest - ing, They have left their house of clay;
But there soon will dawn the morn-ing Of a long un - bro-ken day,

Gone, the lone - ly ech-oes an - swer, Far a - way, yes, far a - way;
They have reached the gold-en sum - mit, Far a - way, yes, far a - way;
When the heart will find its loved ones, Far a - way, yes, far a - way;

Gone, the lone - ly ech - oes an - swer, Far a - way, yes, far a - way.
They have reached the gold-en sum - mit, Far a - way, yes, far a - way.
When the heart will find its loved ones, Far a - way, yes, far a - way.

DEAR LITTLE STRANGER

C. H. G.

Chas. H. Gabriel

1. Low in a man-ger—dear lit-tle Stran-ger, Je-sus, the won-der-ful
2. An-gels de-scend-ing, o-ver Him bend-ing, Chant-ed a ten-der and
3. Dear lit-tle Stran-ger, born in a man-ger, Mak-er and Mon-arch, and

Sav-ior, was born; There was none to re-ceive Him, none to be-lieve Him,
si-lent re-frain; Then a won-der-ful sto-ry told of His glo-ry,
Sav-ior of all; I will love Thee for-ev-er! grieve Thee? no, nev-er!

CHORUS

None but the an-gels were watch-ing that morn.
Un-to the shepherds on Beth-le-hem's plain.
Thou didst for me make Thy bed in a stall.

Dear'lit-tle Stran-ger,

slept in a man-ger. No down-y pil-low un-der His head;

But with the poor He slumbered secure, The dear lit-tle Babe in His bed.

TELL IT AGAIN

BY PERMISSION

Mrs. M. B. C. Slade
R. M. McIntosh

1. In - to the tent where a gip - sy boy lay, Dy - ing a - lone at the
2. "Did He so love me, a poor lit - tle boy? Send un - to me the good
3. Bend-ing we caught the last words of his breath, Just as he en-tered the
4. Smil-ing, he said, as his last sigh he spent, "I am so glad that for

close of the day, News of sal - va - tion we car - ried, said he:
ti - dings of joy? Need I not per - ish? my hand will He hold?
val - ley of death:"God sent His Son!" "Who-so - ev - er," said He:
me He was sent!" Whis-pered, while low sank the sun in the west,

REFRAIN

"No - bod - y ev - er has told it to me!"
No - bod - y ev - er the sto - ry has told!" Tell it a - gain!
"Then I am sure that He sent Him for me!"
"Lord, I be - lieve, tell it now to the rest!"

Tell it a - gain! Sal - va-tion's sto - ry re-peat o'er and o'er, Till none can

say of the chil-dren of men, "No-bod - y ev - er has told me be - fore."

22 SOME DAY, SOMEWHERE

Irma B. Matthews

Geo. F. Rosche

Moderato

Prelude pp

rit.

DUET mf

1. Some day the journey will be done, Some-where we'll find a prom-ised rest;
2. Some day we'll meet our loved and lost, Some-where in some far bright-er land;
3. Some day our Lord will call us home, Some-where we'll lay our bur - den down;

Some day all sor-row turn to joy, Some-where, some day we shall be blessed.
Some day we'll sing the new, new song, And join with praise an angel band.
Some day, if we have faith-ful been, Some-where we will re-ceive a crown.

REFRAIN

Some day, some day, Some-where, the place we can-not see;

Some day, some day, Some-where the Sav - ior waits for me.

23 I'M A PILGRIM

Mary S. B. Dana

J. B. Herbert

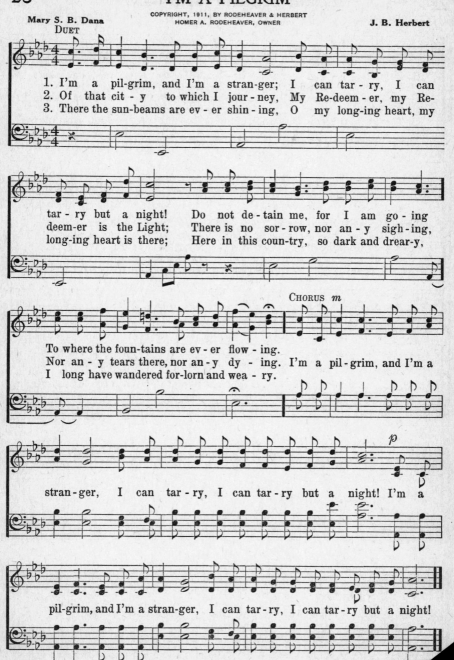

1. I'm a pil-grim, and I'm a stran-ger; I can tar-ry, I can
2. Of that cit - y to which I jour-ney, My Re-deem - er, my Re-
3. There the sun-beams are ev - er shin - ing, O my long-ing heart, my

tar - ry but a night! Do not de - tain me, for I am go - ing
deem-er is the Light; There is no sor - row, nor an - y sigh-ing,
long-ing heart is there; Here in this coun-try, so dark and drear-y,

To where the foun-tains are ev - er flow - ing.
Nor an - y tears there, nor an-y dy - ing. I'm a pil-grim, and I'm a
I long have wandered for-lorn and wea - ry.

stran - ger, I can tar - ry, I can tar - ry but a night! I'm a

pil-grim, and I'm a stran-ger, I can tar - ry, I can tar-ry but a night!

SOME BRIGHT MORNING

24

CHARLOTTE G. HOMER

CHAS. H. GABRIEL

1. Be not a-wea-ry, for la-bor will cease Some glad morn-ing;
2. Wea-ri-some bur-dens will all be laid down, Some glad morn-ing;
3. La-bor well done shall re-ceive its re-ward, Some glad morn-ing;
4. O what a time of re-joic-ing will come, Some glad morn-ing;
5. There with the loved ones who've gone on be-fore, Some glad morn-ing;

Tur-moil will change in-to in-fi-nite peace, Some bright morn-ing.
Then shall our cross be exchanged for a crown, Some bright morn-ing.
Thou who art faith-ful shall be with the Lord, Some bright morn-ing.
When all the ransomed are gathered at home, Some bright morn-ing.
We shall sing praise to the Lamb ev-er-more, Some bright morn-ing.

CHORUS

Some bright morning, Some glad morn-ing, When the sun is shin-ing

in th' e-ter-nal sky; .... Some bright morn-ing, Some glad

cres.

morn-ing .. We shall see the Lord of Har-vest, By and by.

25 SOMEBODY ELSE NEEDS HIM, TOO

Susan R. Peck

B. D. Ackley

1. If you've found Je-sus the Friend that you need, If He is lov-ing and
2. If you are hap-py, and praise fills your heart, Trust Him to car-ry you
3. If you have comfort in be-ing God's child, If He is faith-ful to
4. When the Lord gives you His love and His care, Something He gives you to

true, If you have found Him a Sav-ior in-deed, Some-bod-y
through; If He His Spir-it and love can im-part, Some-bod-y
you, Think, when you see those whom sin has de-filed, Some-bod-y
do; You have the gos-pel with oth-ers to share, Some-bod-y

CHORUS.

else needs Him, too. . . . . Some-bod-y somewhere, perhaps at your side;
needs Him, too.

Some-one is wait-ing for you; . . . . Say that for all Je-sus
yes, wait-ing for you;

suf-fered and died; They need Him, they need Him, too. . . . .
they need Him, too.

26 I THINK WHEN I READ THAT SWEET STORY

Jemima Luke

Davenant. Arr. Hubert P. Main

1. I think when I read that sweet sto-ry of old, When Je-sus was
2. Yet still to His foot-stool in prayer I may go, And ask for a
3. But thou-sands and thousands who wan-der and fall, Nev-er heard of that

here a-mong men; How He called lit-tle chil-dren like lambs to His fold;
share in His love: And if I thus ear-nest-ly seek Him be-low,
heav-en-ly home; I should like them to know there is room for them all,

I should like to have been with Him then! I wish that His hands had been
I shall see Him and hear Him a-bove. In that beau-ti-ful place He is
And that Je-sus has bid them to come. I long for the joy of that

placed on my head, That His arms had been thrown around me, And that I might have
gone to pre-pare For all that are washed and forgiv'n; And man-y dear
glo-ri-ous time, The sweet-est, the brightest, the best, When the dear lit-tle

seen His kind look when He said, "Let the lit-tle ones come un-to Me."
chil-dren are gath-er-ing there, "For of such is the King-dom of Heav'n."
chil-dren of ev-er-y clime Shall crowd to His arms and be blest!

27 TEACH ME TO PRAY

Albert Simpson Reitz   Albert Simpson Reitz

1. Teach me to pray, Lord, teach me to pray; This is my
2. Pow - er in prayer, Lord, pow - er in prayer, Here 'mid earth's
3. My weak-ened will, Lord, Thou canst re - new; My sin - ful
4. Teach me to pray, Lord, teach me to pray; Thou art my

heart - cry, day un - to day; I long to know Thy will and Thy way;
sin and sor-row and care; Men lost and dy - ing, souls in de - spair:
na - ture Thou canst sub-due; Fill me just now with pow - er a - new:
Pat - tern, day un - to day; Thou art my Sure - ty, now and for aye;

CHORUS

Teach me to pray, Lord, teach me to pray.
O give me pow - er, pow - er in prayer! Liv-ing in Thee, Lord,
Pow - er to pray, and pow-er to do!
Teach me to pray, Lord, teach me to pray.

and Thou in me; Con-stant a - bid - ing, this is my plea; Grant me Thy

pow - er, boundless and free: Pow-er with men and pow-er with Thee.

28 IS HE YOURS?

COPYRIGHT, 1930, BY HOMER A. RODEHEAVER
INTERNATIONAL COPYRIGHT SECURED

George O. Webster

Chas. H. Gabriel

1. Je - sus is a friend of mine, Is He yours, is He yours? Friend un-
2. Je - sus is the sinner's friend—Is He yours, is He yours? His is
3. You will need this friend one day—Is He yours, is He yours? Need Him

fail - ing, friend di-vine, Is He yours, is He yours? In the hour of great-est
love that has no end—Is it yours, is it yours? Once He took the sinner's
as your strength and stay, Is He yours, is He yours? When your earthly race is

need He will prove a friend in-deed; Heal - er of all hearts that bleed—
place, Love re-flect - ing in His face! Oh, the won - ders of His grace—
run, When you face life's set-ting sun, Would you miss His glad "well done"—

CHORUS

Is He yours?
Is it yours? Is He yours—this friend of mine? Is He yours, this friend di-
Is He yours?

vine? Faith-ful, lov - ing, loy - al, kind— Is He yours, is He yours?

29 AT THE END OF THE ROAD

A. H. A.

Rev. A. H. Ackley

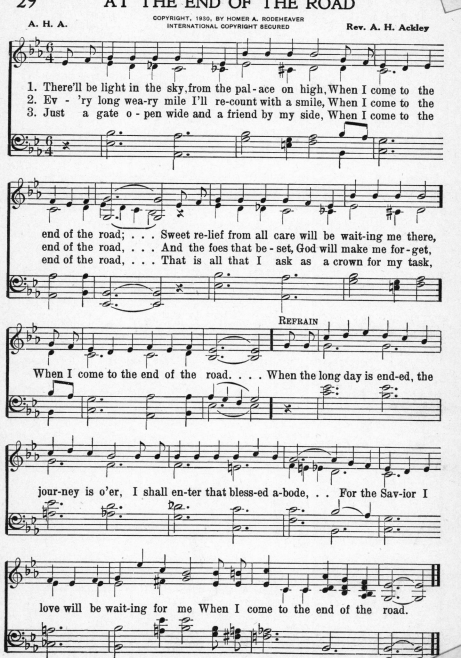

1. There'll be light in the sky, from the pal-ace on high, When I come to the
2. Ev - 'ry long wea-ry mile I'll re-count with a smile, When I come to the
3. Just a gate o - pen wide and a friend by my side, When I come to the

end of the road; . . . Sweet re-lief from all care will be wait-ing me there,
end of the road, . . . And the foes that be - set, God will make me for-get,
end of the road, . . . That is all that I ask as a crown for my task,

REFRAIN

When I come to the end of the road. . . . When the long day is end-ed, the

jour-ney is o'er, I shall en-ter that bless-ed a-bode, . . . For the Sav-ior I

love will be wait-ing for me When I come to the end of the road.

30   O, WHAT A WONDERFUL SAVIOR

A. H. A.

Rev. A. H. Ackley

1. I have a Friend who a - bides in my heart, O, what a won-der-ful
2. Nev-er a foe that His eye can-not see, O, what a won-der-ful
3. He will the vil - est of sin-ners for-give, O, what a won-der-ful
4. There is a home at the end of life's way, O, what a won-der-ful

Sav - ior! I can - not live from His pres-ence a - part, O, what a
Sav - ior! Nev-er a mo-ment that He for-gets me, O, what a
Sav - ior! No heart so dead but His touch can make live, O, what a
Sav - ior! Where in His pres-ence for - ev - er I'll stay, O, what a

CHORUS

won - der - ful Sav - ior! O, what a won - der - ful Sav - ior is He,

Won - der of won - ders that He should love me! Some day His glo - ri - ous

face I shall see, . . . O, what a won - der - ful Sav - ior!

31   WILL THE CIRCLE BE UNBROKEN?

Ada R. Habershon

Chas. H. Gabriel

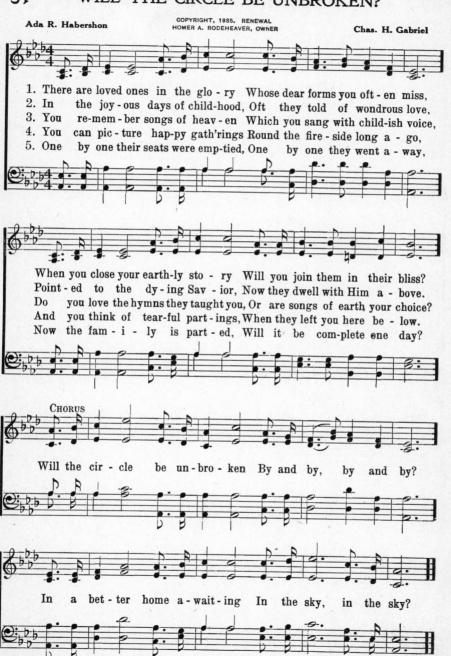

1. There are loved ones in the glo-ry Whose dear forms you oft-en miss,
2. In the joy-ous days of child-hood, Oft they told of wondrous love,
3. You re-mem-ber songs of heav-en Which you sang with child-ish voice,
4. You can pic-ture hap-py gath'rings Round the fire-side long a-go,
5. One by one their seats were emp-tied, One by one they went a-way,

When you close your earth-ly sto-ry Will you join them in their bliss?
Point-ed to the dy-ing Sav-ior, Now they dwell with Him a-bove.
Do you love the hymns they taught you, Or are songs of earth your choice?
And you think of tear-ful part-ings, When they left you here be-low.
Now the fam-i-ly is part-ed, Will it be com-plete one day?

CHORUS

Will the cir-cle be un-bro-ken By and by, by and by?

In a bet-ter home a-wait-ing In the sky, in the sky?

AFTER A WHILE

32

T. O. Chisholm

B. D. Ackley

SOLO. *With expression*

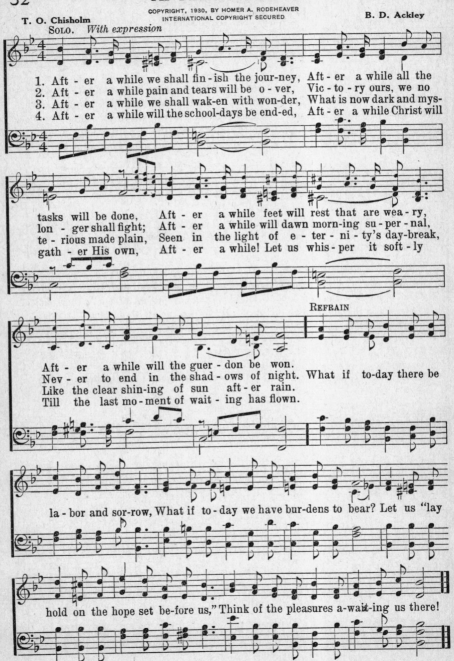

1. Aft - er   a while we shall fin - ish the jour-ney,   Aft - er   a while all the
2. Aft - er   a while pain and tears will be o - ver,   Vic - to - ry ours, we no
3. Aft - er   a while we shall wak-en with won-der,   What is now dark and mys-
4. Aft - er   a while will the school-days be end-ed,   Aft - er   a while Christ will

tasks   will be done,   Aft - er   a while feet will rest that are wea - ry,
lon - ger shall fight;   Aft - er   a while will dawn morn-ing su - per - nal,
te - rious made plain,   Seen in   the light of e - ter - ni - ty's day-break,
gath - er His own,   Aft - er   a while! Let us whis - per it soft - ly

REFRAIN

Aft - er   a while will the guer - don be won.
Nev - er   to end in the shad - ows of night. What if to-day there be
Like the clear shin-ing of sun   aft - er rain.
Till   the last mo - ment of wait - ing has flown.

la - bor and sor-row, What if to - day we have bur-dens to bear? Let us "lay

hold on the hope set be-fore us," Think of the pleasures a-wait-ing us there!

33 THE NAME OF JESUS

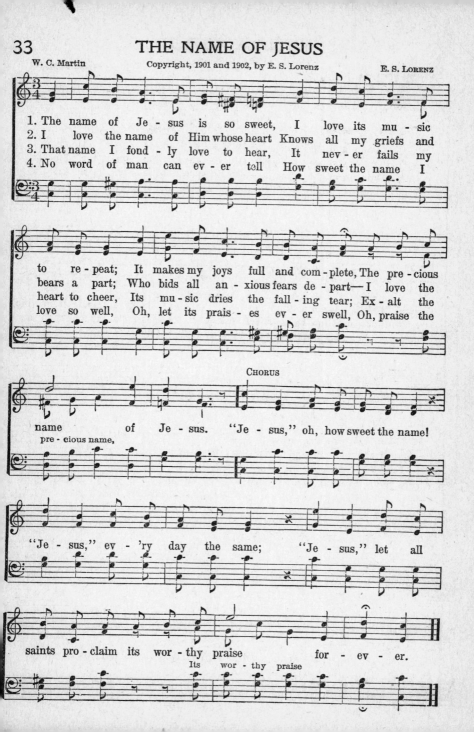

34 I KNOW A NAME

Haldor Lillenas

Haldor Lillenas

SOLO. *Soprano*

1. I know a name that can drive a-way all sor-row, I know a
2. I know a name that can still the rag-ing tem-pest, I know a
3. I know a name that dis-pels the pow'rs of e-vil, I know a
4. I know a name, won-drous name a-bove all oth-ers, O sa-cred

name that is sweet-er than them all; I know a name from which
name that can calm the troub-led sea; I know a name with a
name that can break the tempt-er's snare; I know a name that un-
name by an-gel-ic hosts a-dored; I know a name that is

com-fort I may bor-row When oth-ers fail and when tears of an-guish fall.
ten-der touch of heal-ing For ev-'ry heart that by sin may troub-led be.
locks the gate of heav-en When thro' its mer-its I go to God in prayer.
al-to-geth-er love-ly, O pre-cious name of my liv-ing Christ and Lord.

REFRAIN *rit.* — — — — — — *a tempo*

I know a name, a won-der-ful name, That won-der-ful name is Je - sus.

35 MY SOUL DELIGHTS

Gertrude R. Dugan

George S. Schuler

DUET

Introduction

1. I have in heav'n a Friend so dear, Who sends me light and hope and cheer; He gave His precious life for me Up-on the cross of Cal-va-ry.
2. O'er all my way His hand I see Di-rect-ing and up-hold-ing me; No day so full of grief, or care, No night so dark but He is there.
3. And if my bur-den heav-y be, His arm sup-ports my load and me, While o-ver path-ways all un-trod He leads me on and up to God.

REFRAIN

O hal-le-lu-jah! Praise His name! My soul de-lights in Christ my Lord;

O hal-le-lu-jah! Praise His name! My soul de-lights in Christ my Lord.

36 I'LL GO WHERE YOU WANT ME TO GO

MARY BROWN   CARRIE E. ROUNSEFELL

1. It may not be on the mountain height, Or o-ver the storm-y sea,
2. Perhaps to-day there are lov-ing words Which Jesus would have me speak;
3. There's surely somewhere a low-ly place In earth's harvest fields so wide,

It may not be at the bat-tle's front My Lord will have need of me;
There may be now in the paths of sin Some wand'rer whom I should seek:
Where I may la-bor thro' life's short day For Je-sus, the Cru-ci-fied;

But if, by a still, small voice He calls To paths that I do not know,
O Sav-ior, if Thou wilt be my guide, Tho' dark and rug-ged the way,
So trust-ing my all to Thy ten-der care, And knowing Thou lov-est me,

I'll answer, dear Lord, with my hand in Thine, I'll go where you want me to go.
My voice shall ech-o the mes-sage sweet, I'll say what you want me to say.
I'll do Thy will with a heart sin-cere, I'll be what you want me to be.

REFRAIN

I'll go where you want me to go, dear Lord, Over mountain, or plain, or sea;

I'LL GO WHERE YOU WANT ME TO GO

I'll say what you want me to say, dear Lord, I'll be what you want me to be.

37 TRANSFORMED

Copyright, 1920, by Homer A. Rodeheaver
International copyright secured

Mrs. F. G. Burroughs

B. D. Ackley

1. Dear Lord, take up my tan-gled strands, Where we have wrought in vain,
2. Touch Thou the sad, dis-cord-ant keys Of ev-'ry troub-led breast,
3. Where bro-ken vows in frag-ments lie— The toll of wast-ed years,—
4. Take all the fail-ures, each mis-take Of our poor, hu-man ways,

That by the skill of Thy dear hands Some beau-ty may re-main.
And change to peace-ful har-mo-nies The sigh-ings of un-rest.
Do Thou make whole a-gain, we cry, And give a song for tears.
Then, Sav-ior, for Thine own dear sake, Make them show forth Thy praise.

CHORUS

Transformed by grace di-vine, The glo - - ry shall be Thine;
Trans-formed The glo-ry

To Thy most ho-ly will, O Lord, We now our all re-sign.

THE ROSE OF SHARON

H. R. Palmer

H. R. Palmer

1. There's a Rose that is blooming for you, friend, There's a Rose that is blooming for me;
2. Long a-go in the val-ley so fair, friend, Far a-way by the beau-ti-ful sea,
3. All in vain did they crush this fair flow'r, friend, All in vain did they shatter the tree,

Its per-fume is per-vad-ing the world, friend, Its per-fume is for you and for me.
This pure Rose in its beauty first bloomed, friend, And it blooms still for you and for me.
For its roots, deeply bedded, sprang forth, friend, And it blooms still for you and for me.

REFRAIN

There's a Rose,............... a love-ly Rose,............... And its
Rose that blooms for me, A Rose that blooms for you,

beau-ty all the world shall see;...... There's a Rose,............... a love-ly
Rose that blooms for me, A

THE ROSE OF SHARON

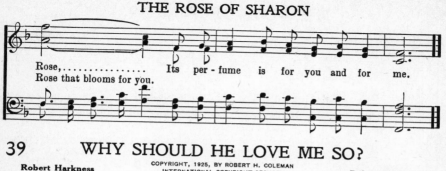

Rose,............... Its per-fume is for you and for me.
Rose that blooms for you.

39 WHY SHOULD HE LOVE ME SO?

Robert Harkness

Robert Harkness

SOLO

1. Love sent my Sav-ior to die in my stead, Why should He love me so?
2. Nails pierced His hands and His feet for my sin, Why should He love me so?
3. O how He ag-o-nized there in my place, Why should He love me so?

Meek-ly to Cal-va-ry's cross He was led, Why should He love me so?......
He suf-fered sore my sal-va-tion to win, Why should He love me so?......
Noth-ing with-hold-ing my sin to ef-face, Why should He love me so?......

CHORUS

Why should He love me so? Why should He love me so?........
love me so?

Why should my Sav-ior to Cal-va-ry go? Why should He love me so?..........
love me so?

40 THE OLD SHIP ZION

M. J. Cartwright

D. B. Towner

Effective Solo

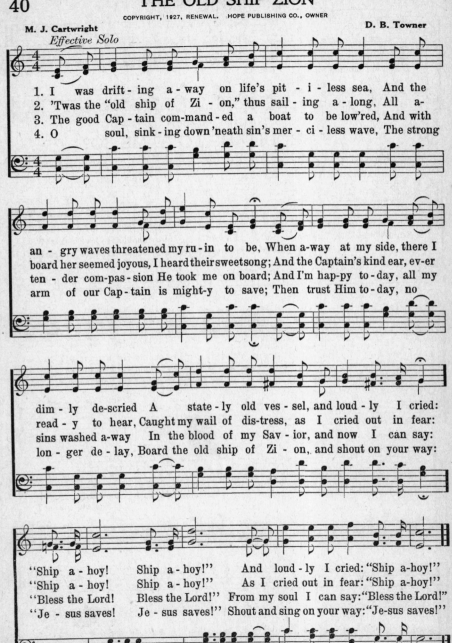

1. I was drift-ing a-way on life's pit-i-less sea, And the
2. 'Twas the "old ship of Zi-on," thus sail-ing a-long, All a-
3. The good Cap-tain com-mand-ed a boat to be low'red, And with
4. O soul, sink-ing down 'neath sin's mer-ci-less wave, The strong

an-gry waves threatened my ru-in to be, When a-way at my side, there I
board her seemed joyous, I heard their sweet song; And the Captain's kind ear, ev-er
ten-der com-pas-sion He took me on board; And I'm hap-py to-day, all my
arm of our Cap-tain is might-y to save; Then trust Him to-day, no

dim-ly de-scried A state-ly old ves-sel, and loud-ly I cried:
read-y to hear, Caught my wail of dis-tress, as I cried out in fear:
sins washed a-way In the blood of my Sav-ior, and now I can say:
lon-ger de-lay, Board the old ship of Zi-on, and shout on your way:

"Ship a-hoy! Ship a-hoy!" And loud-ly I cried: "Ship a-hoy!"
"Ship a-hoy! Ship a-hoy!" As I cried out in fear: "Ship a-hoy!"
"Bless the Lord! Bless the Lord!" From my soul I can say: "Bless the Lord!"
"Je-sus saves! Je-sus saves!" Shout and sing on your way: "Je-sus saves!"

JESUS REMEMBERED YOU

Rev. W. C. Poole

Chas. H. Gabriel

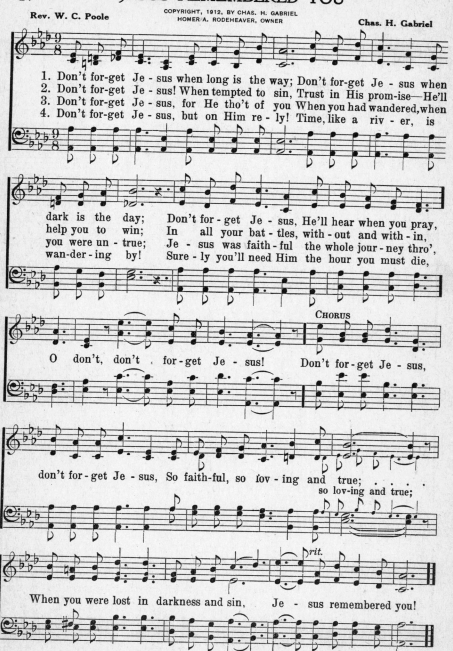

1. Don't for-get Je - sus when long is the way; Don't for-get Je - sus when
2. Don't for-get Je - sus! When tempted to sin, Trust in His prom-ise—He'll
3. Don't for-get Je - sus, for He tho't of you When you had wandered, when
4. Don't for-get Je - sus, but on Him re - ly! Time, like a riv - er, is

dark is the day; Don't for-get Je - sus, He'll hear when you pray,
help you to win; In all your bat - tles, with - out and with - in,
you were un - true; Je - sus was faith - ful the whole jour - ney thro',
wan-der - ing by! Sure - ly you'll need Him the hour you must die,

CHORUS

O don't, don't for-get Je - sus! Don't for-get Je - sus,

don't for-get Je - sus, So faith-ful, so lov-ing and true;
so lov-ing and true;

rit.

When you were lost in darkness and sin, Je - sus remembered you!

42 JESUS WILL!

Ina Duley Ogdon

B. D. Ackley

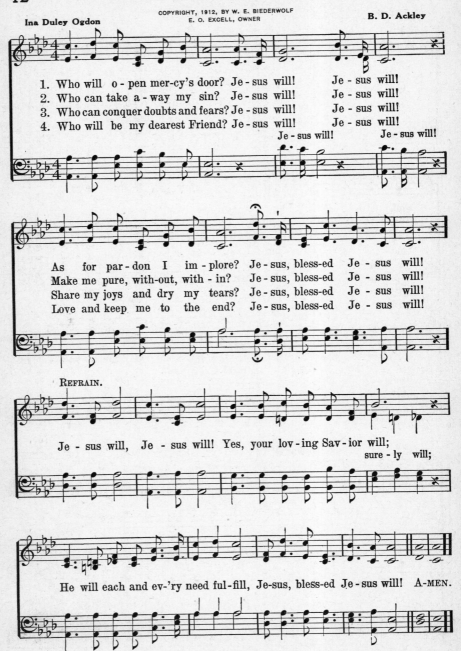

1. Who will o - pen mer-cy's door? Je - sus will! Je - sus will!
2. Who can take a - way my sin? Je - sus will! Je - sus will!
3. Who can conquer doubts and fears? Je - sus will! Je - sus will!
4. Who will be my dearest Friend? Je - sus will! Je - sus will!

Je - sus will! Je - sus will!

As   for par - don I im - plore? Je - sus, bless-ed Je - sus will!
Make me pure, with-out, with - in? Je - sus, bless-ed Je - sus will!
Share my joys and dry my tears? Je - sus, bless-ed Je - sus will!
Love and keep me to the end? Je - sus, bless-ed Je - sus will!

REFRAIN.

Je - sus will, Je - sus will! Yes, your lov - ing Sav - ior will;

sure - ly will;

He will each and ev - 'ry need ful - fill, Je - sus, bless-ed Je - sus will! A-MEN.

43 WHY DO I LOVE HIM?

Rev. Elisha A. Hoffman

James C. Moore

1. Why do I love Him, my Sav-ior and King? Why in my glad-ness of
2. Why is my heart such a well-spring of peace? Why am I blest with con-
3. Why do the days seem so won-drous-ly bright? Why is my be-ing so
4. Why have I rest as the days roll a-long? Why thrills my soul with such

soul do I sing? This is my joy-ful-ness—Je-sus is mine!
tent-ment like this? Je-sus has gra-cious-ly an-swered my prayer,
flood-ed with light? Je-sus, the Day-star, is ris-en with-in,
ju-bi-lant song? Je-sus, my Lord and my Sav-ior di-vine,

CHORUS

For in my heart dwells this Sav-ior di-vine.
Made me the child of His love and His care.   O 'tis a won-der-ful
And I am bur-dened no more with my sin.
Has made His home in this saved heart of mine.

life so to live, Each passing moment new grace to re-ceive, Hav-ing sweet

peace and con-tent-ment al-way, Walking with Je-sus from day un-to day!

44 THE CHURCH BY THE SIDE OF THE ROAD

Rev. W. C. Poole   B. D. Ackley

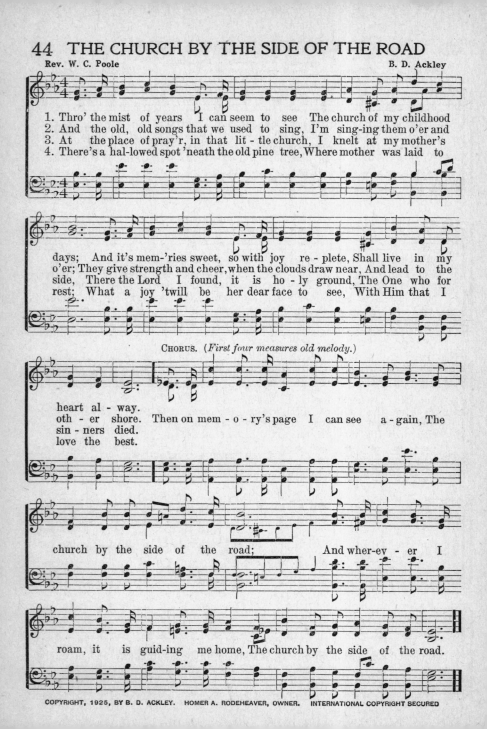

1. Thro' the mist of years I can seem to see The church of my childhood
2. And the old, old songs that we used to sing, I'm sing-ing them o'er and
3. At the place of pray'r, in that lit - tle church, I knelt at my mother's
4. There's a hal-lowed spot 'neath the old pine tree, Where mother was laid to

days; And it's mem-'ries sweet, so with joy re - plete, Shall live in my
o'er; They give strength and cheer, when the clouds draw near, And lead to the
side, There the Lord I found, it is ho - ly ground, The One who for
rest; What a joy 'twill be her dear face to see, With Him that I

CHORUS. (*First four measures old melody.*)

heart al - way.
oth - er shore. Then on mem - o - ry's page I can see a - gain, The
sin - ners died.
love the best.

church by the side of the road; And wher-ev - er I

roam, it is guid-ing me home, The church by the side of the road.

45 ONE MOMENT IN HEAVEN

L. S. L.

Lida Shivers Leech

DUET. *Espressivo*

1. The day may be drear-y, the way may seem long, All si - lent the
2. Yes, some-times I long for a glimpse of His face, Who saved me by
3. One mo-ment in heav-en will pay for it all, No sor - row of

soul's cheer-ing song; But when we a-wake on that beau-ti - ful shore, All
won - der - ful grace; But some day my dream will come true and I'll see My
earth we'll re - call; For - ev - er we'll dwell in that Cit - y of Gold, And

sor - row and pain will be o'er.
Sav - ior who suf - fered for me.
feast on its glo - ries un - told.

CHORUS

One mo-ment in heav-en will pay for it all, When low at the feet of the King I shall fall; Tho' tri-als of earth oft my soul have enthralled, One moment in heaven will pay for it all.

46 THE SWEET OLD SONGS I HEARD MY MOTHER SING

A. J. Hodge

A. J. Hodge

SOLO

1. When the twi-light soft-ly gath-ers, and a hush is on the air, When the
2. I re-mem-ber when she sang to me of Je-sus and His love, And that
3. Now a-gain I see her smil-ing, as I stand be-side her knee, And a-

voice of man and nature seem to pause in qui-et prayer, Then a-mong the man-y
we should strive to meet Him in the shining courts above: How it thrilled my heart to
gain I hear the sweet old songs she used to sing to me; But a peace is steal-ing

whis-pers that the coming shadows bring, I hear a-gain the sweet old songs I
hear her in that hap-py, hap-py day; But soon I had for-got-ten and had
o - ver, as the night is drawing in, For I've promised I will meet her in the

CHORUS

heard my mother sing.
wan-dered far a - way. O the sweet old songs I heard my moth-er sing, What
pal - ace of the King.

mem - o - ries they bring, sweet memories they bring! In my dreams when all the

THE SWEET OLD SONGS I HEARD MY MOTHER SING

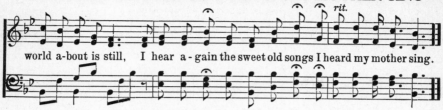

world a-bout is still, I hear a-gain the sweet old songs I heard my mother sing.

47 WHAT WILL YOU DO WITH JESUS?

"What shall I do then with Jesus, which is called Christ?"—MATT. 27: 22

COPYRIGHT, 1905, BY CHARLES M. ALEXANDER. INTERNATIONAL COPYRIGHT SECURED
HOPE PUB. CO., OWNER

Anon.   M. L. Stocks

1. Je - sus is standing in Pilate's hall—Friendless, for-sak-en, betrayed by all:
2. Je - sus is standing on tri - al still, You can be false to Him if you will,
3. Will you e-vade Him as Pi-late tried? Or will you choose Him, whate'er betide?
4. Will you, like Peter, your Lord de-ny? Or will you scorn from His foes to fly,
5. "Je - sus, I give Thee my heart to-day! Je - sus, I'll fol - low Thee all the way,

Heark-en! what meaneth the sud - den call? What will you do with Je - sus?
You can be faith-ful thro' good or ill: What will you do with Je - sus?
Vain - ly you struggle from Him to hide: What will you do with Je - sus?
Dar - ing for Je - sus to live or die? What will you do with Je - sus?
Glad - ly o - bey-ing Thee!" will you say: "This will I do with Je - sus!"

CHORUS

What will you do with Je - sus? Neu - tral you can - not be;

Some day your heart will be ask - ing, "What will He do with me?"

REIGN THOU SUPREME

48

INTERNATIONAL COPYRIGHT, 1925, BY HERBERT G. TOVEY

Albert Simpson Reitz   Albert Simpson Reitz

SOLO OR DUET

1. Hear Thou my prayer, O Sav-ior di - vine;   Come, sat - is - fy this
2. I claim Thy prom - ise, Je - sus my Lord—   Thy bless-ed prom - ise
3. Thy hal-lowed Pres-ence bring-eth de - light,   Brightens my way, il-

heart-cry of mine;   O let my life con - form to Thy will,
in Thy blest Word: That Thou wouldst ev - er with me a - bide,
lu - mines my night;   Floods heart and soul with heav-en - ly song,

CHORUS

Un - til Thy life my soul shall in - fill.
Shel-ter and keep me close to Thy side.   Spir-it of God, O take full con-
And gives me vic - t'ry all the day long.

trol: Thy Pres-ence, now, en - throne in my soul!   Full-ness of

love to me now im - part; Reign Thou supreme, O Lord, in my heart.

MY MOTHER'S HANDS

Mrs. M. E. W.

USED BY PERMISSION

Mrs. M. E. Wilson
Sister of the late P. P. Bliss

Slowly, with great expression

1. { Oh, those beau-ti-ful, beau-ti-ful hands! Tho' they nei-ther were white nor small,
   { Oh, those beau-ti-ful, beau-ti-ful hands! How they cared for my in - fant days;

2. { Oh, those beau-ti-ful, beau-ti-ful hands! As they pressed my ach - ing brow,
   { Oh, those beau-ti-ful, beau-ti-ful hands! Thin and wrinkled with age they grew;

3. { Oh, those beau-ti-ful, beau-ti-ful hands! I stood by her cof - fin one day,
   { Oh, those beau-ti-ful, beau-ti-ful hands! I shall clasp them a - gain once more,

Yet my moth - er's hands were the fair - est And love - li - est hands of all.
They guid-ed my feet in - to pleasant paths, And smoothed all the rug - ged ways.
They cooled the fe - ver and eased the pain, Me - thinks I can feel them now.
But still they toiled on for the child so dear, And her love seemed more tender and true.
And I kissed those hands so cold and white, As qui - et and peaceful she lay;
As my feet touch the bank of the heav'nly land, We shall meet on that shin - ing shore.

CHORUS

My mother's dear hands, her beau-ti - ful hands, Which guarded me safe o'er life's sands;

I bless God's name for the mem - 'ry Of moth-er's own beau-ti - ful hands.

MY MOTHER'S PRAYER

BY PERMISSION OF IRA D. SANKEY, OWNER OF COPYRIGHT

"Her children arise up, and call her blessed"—PROV. 21: 28

T. C. O'Kane

T. C. O'Kane

SOLO. *Moderato*

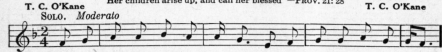

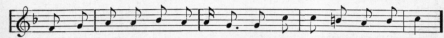

1. As I wan-dered 'round the homestead, Man-y a dear fa-mil-iar spot
2. Tho' the house was held by stran-gers, All remained the same with-in;
3. Quick I drew it from the rub-bish, Cov-ered o'er with dust so long:

Bro't with-in my rec-ol-lec-tion Scenes I'd seem-ing-ly for-got;
Just as when a child I ram-bled Up and down, and out and in;
When, be-hold, I heard in fan-cy Strains of one fa-mil-iar song,

There, the orchard—mead-ow, yon-der—Here, the deep, old fash-ioned well,
To the gar-ret dark as-cend-ing—Once a source of child-ish dread—
Oft-en sung by my dear moth-er To me in that trun-dle bed;

rit.

With its old moss-cov-ered buck-et, Sent a thrill no tongue can tell.
Peer-ing thro' the mist-y cob-webs, Lo! I saw my trun-dle bed.
[Omit.................

Second Ending. Slowly p
pp

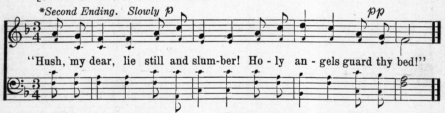

"Hush, my dear, lie still and slum-ber! Ho-ly an-gels guard thy bed!"

4 While I listen to the music
  Stealing on in gentle strain,
I am carried back to childhood—
  I am now a child again:
'Tis the hour of my retiring,
  At the dusky eventide;
Near my trundle bed I'm kneeling,
  As of yore, by mother's side.

5 Hands are on my head so loving,
  As they were in childhood's days;
I, with weary tones, am trying
  To repeat the words she says;
'Tis a prayer in language simple
  As a mother's lips can frame:
*"Father, Thou who art in heaven,
  Hallowed, ever, be Thy name."

  *Use second ending

6 Prayer is over: to my pillow
  With a "good-night!" kiss I creep,
Scarcely waking while I whisper,
  "Now I lay me down to sleep,"
Then my mother, o'er me bending,
  Prays in earnest words, but mild:
*"Hear my prayer, O heavenly Father,
  Bless, O bless, my precious child!"

7 Yet I am but only dreaming:
  Ne'er I'll be a child again;
Many years has that dear mother
  In the quiet churchyard lain;
But the mem'ry of her counsels
  O'er my path a light has shed,
Daily calling me to heaven,
  Even from my trundle bed.

51 SOMEBODY HERE NEEDS JESUS

James Rowe

Harry Dixon Loes

1. Some-bod-y here is wea-ry and worn, Bend-ing be-neath a
2. Some-bod-y here is wea-ry of sin, Long-ing to let the
3. Some-bod-y here will an-swer His plea, Kneel at His feet, a
4. Some-bod-y here is look-ing a-bove, Read-y to trust His

bur-den long borne; Tired of the storms and thorns on the way,
Bless-ed One in; Read-y to take the heav-en-ly way,
Chris-tian to be; Some-bod-y here for par-don will pray,
mer-cy and love; Know-ing what dan-ger lies in de-lay,

CHORUS.

Some-bod-y here needs Je-sus to-day. Some-bod-y here is

sad and a-lone, Some-one whose song and laughter have flown; Come, He'll re-

ceive you, He will re-lieve you, Some-bod-y here needs Je-sus to-day.

ONE SWEETLY SOLEMN THOUGHT

ARRANGEMENT COPYRIGHT, 1930, BY HOMER A. RODEHEAVER

Phoebe Cary

R. S. Ambrose
Arranged

Andante

One sweetly sol-emn tho't Comes to me o'er and o'er,— I am near-er

home to-day Than I've ev-er been be-fore. Near-er my Father's house, Where the

man-y mansions be; Near-er the great white throne, Near-er the crystal sea;

Near-er the bounds of life, Where we lay our burdens down; Near-er leav-ing the

cross, Near-er gain-ing the crown. But, ly-ing dark-ly be-tween,

ONE SWEETLY SOLEMN THOUGHT

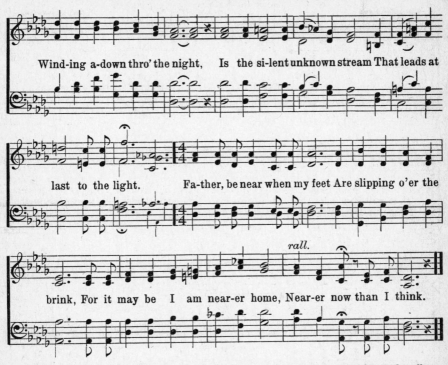

Wind-ing a-down thro' the night,   Is the si-lent unknown stream That leads at
last to the light.   Fa-ther, be near when my feet Are slipping o'er the
brink, For it may be   I am near-er home, Near-er now than I think.

An appropriate Grace before meals, to be sung or recited by a leader or by all

 53   ## BETHANY BLESSING

Dedicated to the Bethany Girls

Carrie Stewart-Besserer   B. D. Ackley

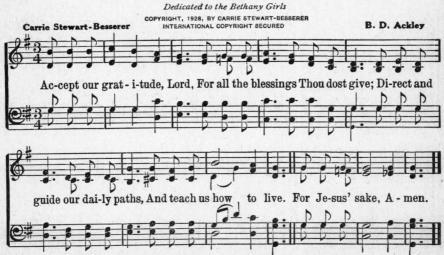

Ac-cept our grat - i-tude, Lord, For all the blessings Thou dost give; Di-rect and
guide our dai-ly paths, And teach us how   to live. For Je-sus' sake, A - men.

RAISE ME, JESUS, TO THY BOSOM

COPYRIGHT, 1885, BY W. F. SHAW
USED BY PERMISSION

Birdseye

Wm. A. Huntley

DUET

1. Raise me, Je-sus, to Thy bos-om, From this world of sin and woes;
2. Raise me, Je-sus, to Thy bos-om, For my heart is slave to fear,
3. Raise me, Je-sus, to Thy bos-om, Hear a con-trite spirit's prayer;

Let me feel Thine arms a-round me, Then my soul may know re-pose.
That will van-ish as a shad-ow, When it feels Thy pres-ence near.
Raise me from the sin a-round me, Ere I yield me to de-spair.

SOLO

I am wea-ry with my bur-den, And I come to Thee for rest; Kneel-ing
In my an-guish deign to hear me All my sin and grief con-fess; By the
O I feel that Thou wilt hear me, And wilt give me ho-ly rest; Now I

at Thy feet, I pray Thee Lift me, Je-sus, to Thy breast.
prom-ise Thou hast giv-en, Lift me, Je-sus, to Thy breast.
feel Thy glo-ry near me, Lift me, Je-sus, to Thy breast.

QUARTET OR CHORUS

Raise me, Je-sus, to Thy bos-om, From this world of sin and woes;

RAISE ME, JESUS, TO THY BOSOM

Let me feel Thine arms a-round me, Then my soul may know re-pose.

55   I'LL GO WITH YOU

Gerald E. Bonney

COPYRIGHT, 1928, BY GERALD E. BONNEY

Gerald E. Bonney

1. When I start up-on the jour-ney, At the break-ing of the day,
2. When the road is hot and dust-y, And I rest at heat of day,
3. When the eve-ning shadows gath-er, At the clos-ing of the day,
4. When the shades of night have vanished, And I wake in end-less day,

Je-sus cheers my soul by whis-p'ring, "I'll go with you all the way."
I can hear that same voice whis-per, "I'll go with you all the way."
Je-sus whis-pers in the twi-light, "I've been with you all the way."
I will meet the bless-ed Sav-ior, Who went with me all the way.

CHORUS

I'll go with you all the way, I'll go with you all the day;

O how pre-cious when He whis-pers, "I'll go with you all the way."

56 SUNSET DAYS

William M. Runyan

Harry Dixon Loes

DUET

1. Aft - er life's fe - ver, its toil and its care, Aft - er its bur-dens so
2. Sweet is the tho't, when life's bat-tle is hard, When fond am-bi-tions are
3. Hope thou in God ev - 'ry step of the way, He on your brow will His

heav - y to bear, Aft - er its noon-tide, its heat and its glare, Come, with their
bro - ken and marred, When the tired spir-it with con-flict is scarred,— Aft - er a-
hand gen-tly lay; God will bend o - ver you, lov-ing al-way, E'en to the

bless-ings life's sun - set days.
while come life's sun - set days.
end of life's sun - set days.

REFRAIN

Days that bring qui-et, dear days that breathe

peace, Days that from strug-gle bring gra-cious re - lease; When in the

heart hopes of heav-en in-crease, Beau - ti - ful, bless - ed sun - set days.

SUNSET DAYS

CODA

Sun - set days, *(beau-ti-ful)* sun - set days, Beau - ti - ful sun - set days!

God's gift from a-bove, His to-ken of love, *(are God's)* Beau-ti-ful sun - set days.

57 JESUS HAS LOVED ME

J. Wakefield MacGill

Antoine E. Batiste

1. Je - sus has loved me— won - der - ful Sav - ior! Je - sus has
2. Je - sus has saved me— won - der - ful Sav - ior! Je - sus has
3. Je - sus will lead me— won - der - ful Sav - ior! Je - sus will

loved me, I can - not tell why; ... He came to res - cue
saved me, I can - not tell how; ... But this I do know,
lead me, I can - not tell where; .. So I will fol - low

sin - ners un-wor - thy; My heart He conquered, for Him I would die.
He came, my ran-som, Dy - ing on Cal - v'ry with thorns on His brow.
thro' joy or sor - row, Sun-shine or tem - pest, since He leads me there.

FACE TO FACE

58

Mrs. Frank A. Breck   RENEWAL, 1927, BY GRANT COLFAX TULLAR, OWNER   Grant Colfax Tullar

Moderato.

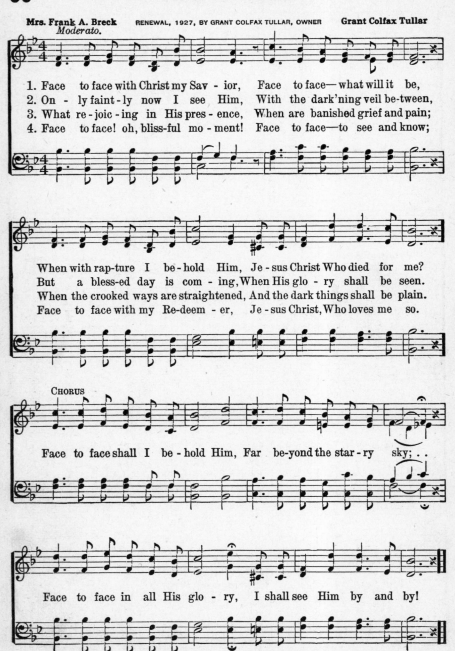

1. Face to face with Christ my Sav - ior, Face to face—what will it be,
2. On - ly faint - ly now I see Him, With the dark'ning veil be - tween,
3. What re - joic - ing in His pres - ence, When are banished grief and pain;
4. Face to face! oh, bliss-ful mo - ment! Face to face—to see and know;

When with rap-ture I be - hold Him, Je - sus Christ Who died for me?
But a bless-ed day is com - ing, When His glo - ry shall be seen.
When the crooked ways are straightened, And the dark things shall be plain.
Face to face with my Re-deem - er, Je - sus Christ, Who loves me so.

CHORUS

Face to face shall I be - hold Him, Far be-yond the star - ry sky; . .

Face to face in all His glo - ry, I shall see Him by and by!

WITH HIM IN GALILEE

H. W. Hawkes
3rd stanza by C. H. G.

Chas. H. Gabriel

DUET *Soprano (or Tenor) and Alto*

1. A - mid the din of earth - ly strife, A - mid the bus - y crowd,
2. I lin - ger near Him in the throng, And lis - ten to His voice;
3. What bless - ed fel - low-ship have we, And how my glad heart thrills,

The whis - pers of e - ter - nal life Are lost in clam - ors loud;
I feel my wea - ry soul grow strong, My sad - dened heart re - joice;
As thus He walks and talks with me And calms life's dark - est ills;

When, lo! I find a heal - ing balm, The world grows dim to me;
A - mid the storms that dark - ly frown I hear His call to me,
No mat - ter how the winds may blow, Or rough life's an - gry sea,

My spir - it rests in sud - den calm With Him in Gal - i - lee.
And lay my wea - ry bur - den down With Him in Gal - i - lee.
'Tis joy to be and heav'n to go With Him in Gal - i - lee.

60 SOMEHOW

DUET FOR SOPRANO AND ALTO

Rev. A. H. A.   Rev. A. H. Ackley

1. Some-how I know that Christ is mine, No pow'r can take me out of His
2. Some-how I feel that He is near, Whene'er I'm tempted to go a-
3. Some-how I hear Him gen-tly call, Whene'er I'm lone-ly and need a
4. Some-how I trust Him for to-day, And for to-mor-row whate'er it

care,   He holds me with His arm di-vine, ... And in His
stray,   His pres-ence calms my ev'-ry fear, ... And keeps me
friend,   His mer-cy lifts me when I fall, ... And will sup-
be,   My anx-ious fears up-on Him lay, ... For Je-sus

King-dom I have a share.
sing-ing a-long the way.   Somehow His love will nev-er let me
port me un-til the end.
watch-es and cares for me.

CHORUS.

go, ... Somehow He loves me better than I know, ... Somehow, some
let me go,   than I know,

day when life is o'er, ... I'll dwell with Him for ev-er-more. ....
life is o'er,   some day.

MESSAGE OF PEACE

61

Thoro Harris

Arr. by T. H

1. Sweet is the old gos-pel sto-ry, Tell-ing of in-fi-nite grace:
2. It is the voice of my Sav-ior Ten-der-ly call-ing to-day,

Je-sus came down from His glo-ry, Suf-fer-ing death in my place!
Trusting a-lone in His fa-vor, En-ter the heav-en-ly way.

O what a great con-de-scen-sion! Wonderful, wonderful love!.......
Then when thy life work is ended An-gels will welcome thee home......

won-der-ful love!
will welcome thee home

dim.

Glo-ry to God in the high-est! Praise to the King from a-bove.
Where, in the highlands of glo-ry, Darkness and death can-not come.

REFRAIN.

Mes - sage of peace,...... O what won - der-ful love,......
Message of peace, message of peace, Wonderful love, wonderful love,

Rais - ing the lost....... To the man - sions a-bove.....
Raising the lost, raising the lost Up to the mansions, the mansions above.

62 HAVE THY WAY, LORD

George Bennard   Rev. George Bennard

Effective as Soprano and Alto Duet

1. Je - sus, see me at Thy feet, With my sac - ri - fice com-plete;
2. O how pa - tient Thou hast been With my pride and in - bred sin!
3. Lord, I loathe my - self and sin, En - ter now and make me clean!
4. Lord, Thy love has won my all, Let Thy Spir - it on me fall;
5. Praise the Lord, the work is done! Praise the Lord, the vic-t'ry's won!

I am bring - ing all to Thee, Thine a - lone I'll be.
O what mer - cy Thou hast shown, Grace and love un - known!
Make my heart just like Thine own; Come, Lord, take Thy throne.
Burn up ev - 'ry trace of sin; Make me pure with - in.
Now the blood is cleans - ing me, From all sin I'm free.

CHORUS

Have Thy way, Lord, have Thy way, This with all my heart I say;

I'll o - bey Thee, come what may; Dear Lord, have Thy way.

63 JESUS, LOVER OF MY SOUL

(Silver Threads Among the Gold)

Charles Wesley

H. P. Danks

1. Je - sus, Lov-er of my soul,   Let me to Thy bos-om fly,
2. Oth - er ref-uge have I none;   Hangs my helpless soul on Thee;
3. Thou, O Christ, art all I want;   More than all in Thee I find;
4. Plenteous grace with Thee is found,   Grace to cov - er all my sin;

While the near - er wa - ters roll,   While the tem-pest still is high.
Leave, oh, leave me not a - lone,   Still sup-port and com-fort me.
Raise the fall - en, cheer the faint,   Heal the sick, and lead the blind.
Let the heal-ing streams a-bound;   Make and keep me pure with-in.

Hide me, O my Sav-ior, hide,   Till the storm of life is past;
All my trust on Thee is stayed,   All my help from Thee I bring;
Just and ho - ly is Thy name,   I am all un-right-eous-ness;
Thou of life the Fountain art,   Free - ly let me take of Thee;

Safe in - to the ha - ven guide,   O re-ceive my soul at last!
Cov - er my de-fense-less head   With the shad-ow of Thy wing.
Vile and full of sin I am,   Thou art full of truth and grace.
Spring Thou up with-in my heart,   Rise to all e - ter - ni - ty.

64 IT'S REAL

H. L. Cox   H. L. Cox

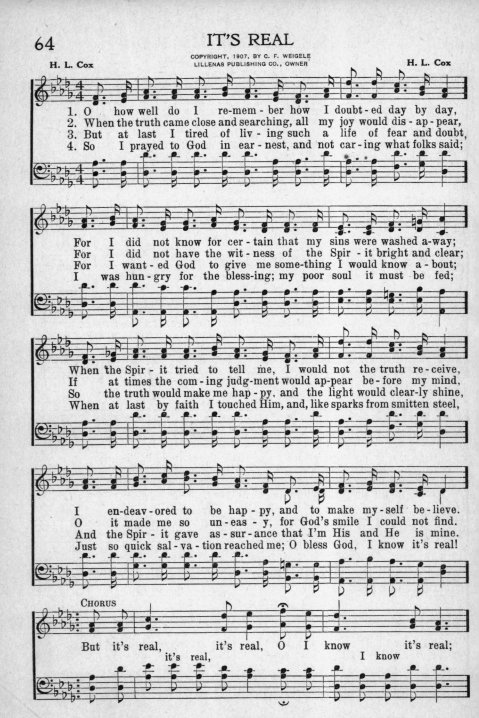

1. O how well do I re-mem-ber how I doubt-ed day by day,
2. When the truth came close and searching, all my joy would dis-ap-pear,
3. But at last I tired of liv-ing such a life of fear and doubt,
4. So I prayed to God in ear-nest, and not car-ing what folks said;

For I did not know for cer-tain that my sins were washed a-way;
For I did not have the wit-ness of the Spir-it bright and clear,
For I want-ed God to give me some-thing I would know a-bout;
I was hun-gry for the bless-ing; my poor soul it must be fed;

When the Spir-it tried to tell me, I would not the truth re-ceive,
If at times the com-ing judg-ment would ap-pear be-fore my mind,
So the truth would make me hap-py, and the light would clear-ly shine,
When at last by faith I touched Him, and, like sparks from smitten steel,

I en-deav-ored to be hap-py, and to make my-self be-lieve.
O it made me so un-eas-y, for God's smile I could not find.
And the Spir-it gave as-sur-ance that I'm His and He is mine.
Just so quick sal-va-tion reached me; O bless God, I know it's real!

CHORUS

But it's real, it's real, O I know it's real;
it's real, I know

IT'S REAL

Praise God, the doubts are set-tled, For I know, I know it's real.

65 NEAR TO THE HEART OF GOD

COPYRIGHT, 1903, BY THE LORENZ PUB. CO.
USED BY PERMISSION

C. B. McAfee

1. There is a place of qui-et rest, Near to the heart of God,
2. There is a place of com-fort sweet, Near to the heart of God,
3. There is a place of full re-lease, Near to the heart of God,

A place where sin can-not mo-lest, Near to the heart of God.
A place where we our Sav-ior meet, Near to the heart of God.
A place where all is joy and peace, Near to the heart of God.

REFRAIN

O Je-sus, blest Re-deem-er, Sent from the heart of God,

Hold us, who wait be-fore Thee, Near to the heart of God.

JESUS, BLESSED JESUS

Chas. H. Gabriel

Chas. H. Gabriel

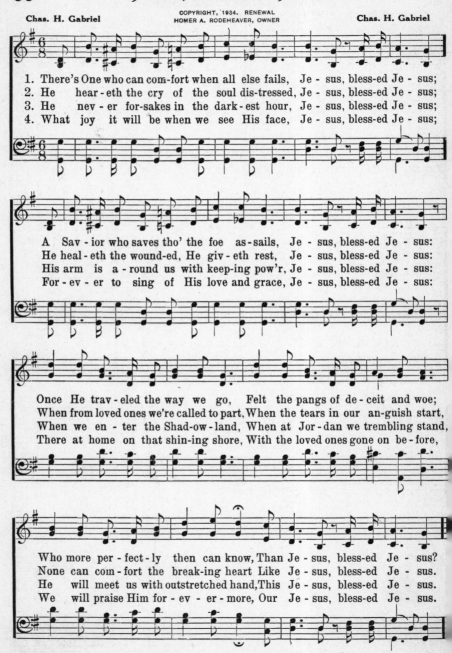

1. There's One who can com-fort when all else fails, Je - sus, bless-ed Je - sus;
2. He hear-eth the cry of the soul dis-tressed, Je - sus, bless-ed Je - sus;
3. He nev - er for-sakes in the dark-est hour, Je - sus, bless-ed Je - sus;
4. What joy it will be when we see His face, Je - sus, bless-ed Je - sus;

A Sav - ior who saves tho' the foe as-sails, Je - sus, bless-ed Je - sus:
He heal-eth the wound-ed, He giv-eth rest, Je - sus, bless-ed Je - sus:
His arm is a - round us with keep-ing pow'r, Je - sus, bless-ed Je - sus:
For - ev - er to sing of His love and grace, Je - sus, bless-ed Je - sus:

Once He trav - eled the way we go, Felt the pangs of de - ceit and woe;
When from loved ones we're called to part, When the tears in our an-guish start,
When we en - ter the Shad-ow-land, When at Jor - dan we trembling stand,
There at home on that shin-ing shore, With the loved ones gone on be - fore,

Who more per - fect - ly then can know, Than Je - sus, bless-ed Je - sus?
None can com - fort the break-ing heart Like Je - sus, bless-ed Je - sus.
He will meet us with outstretched hand, This Je - sus, bless-ed Je - sus.
We will praise Him for - ev - er - more, Our Je - sus, bless-ed Je - sus.

67 INTO MY HEART

Harry D. Clarke

Harry D. Clarke

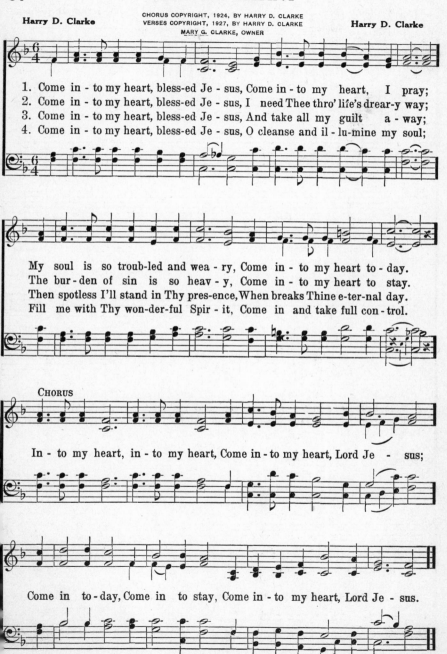

1. Come in - to my heart, bless-ed Je - sus, Come in - to my heart, I pray;
2. Come in - to my heart, bless-ed Je - sus, I need Thee thro' life's drear-y way;
3. Come in - to my heart, bless-ed Je - sus, And take all my guilt a - way;
4. Come in - to my heart, bless-ed Je - sus, O cleanse and il - lu-mine my soul;

My soul is so troub-led and wea - ry, Come in - to my heart to - day.
The bur - den of sin is so heav - y, Come in - to my heart to stay.
Then spotless I'll stand in Thy pres-ence, When breaks Thine e-ter-nal day.
Fill me with Thy won-der-ful Spir - it, Come in and take full con - trol.

CHORUS

In - to my heart, in - to my heart, Come in - to my heart, Lord Je - sus;

Come in to-day, Come in to stay, Come in - to my heart, Lord Je - sus.

68   I WILL NOT DOUBT

J. M. and C. H. G.   Charles H. Gabriel

SOLO

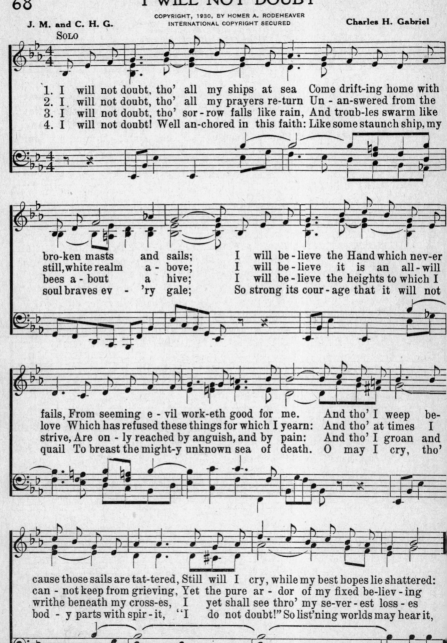

1. I will not doubt, tho' all my ships at sea Come drift-ing home with
2. I will not doubt, tho' all my prayers re-turn Un - an-swered from the
3. I will not doubt, tho' sor - row falls like rain, And troub-les swarm like
4. I will not doubt! Well an-chored in this faith: Like some staunch ship, my

bro-ken masts and sails; I will be - lieve the Hand which nev-er
still, white realm a - bove; I will be - lieve it is an all - will
bees a - bout a hive; I will be - lieve the heights to which I
soul braves ev - 'ry gale; So strong its cour - age that it will not

fails, From seeming e - vil work-eth good for me. And tho' I weep be-
love Which has refused these things for which I yearn: And tho' at times I
strive, Are on - ly reached by anguish, and by pain: And tho' I groan and
quail To breast the might-y unknown sea of death. O may I cry, tho'

cause those sails are tat-tered, Still will I cry, while my best hopes lie shattered:
can - not keep from grieving, Yet the pure ar - dor of my fixed be-liev - ing
writhe beneath my cross-es, I yet shall see thro' my se-ver - est loss - es
bod - y parts with spir - it, "I do not doubt!" So list'ning worlds may hear it,

I WILL NOT DOUBT

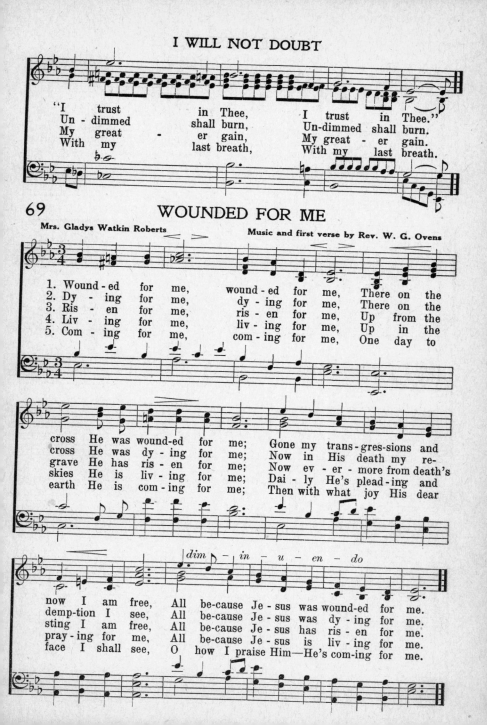

"I trust in Thee, I trust in Thee."
Un - dimmed shall burn, Un-dimmed shall burn.
My great - er gain, My great - er gain.
With my last breath, With my last breath.

69   WOUNDED FOR ME

Mrs. Gladys Watkin Roberts   Music and first verse by Rev. W. G. Ovens

1. Wound-ed for me, wound-ed for me, There on the
2. Dy - ing for me, dy - ing for me, There on the
3. Ris - en for me, ris - en for me, Up from the
4. Liv - ing for me, liv - ing for me, Up in the
5. Com - ing for me, com - ing for me, One day to

cross He was wound-ed for me; Gone my trans-gres-sions and
cross He was dy - ing for me; Now in His death my re-
grave He has ris - en for me; Now ev - er - more from death's
skies He is liv - ing for me; Dai - ly He's plead-ing and
earth He is com - ing for me; Then with what joy His dear

dim - in - u - en - do

now I am free, All be-cause Je - sus was wound-ed for me.
demp-tion I see, All be-cause Je - sus was dy - ing for me.
sting I am free, All be-cause Je - sus has ris - en for me.
pray - ing for me, All be-cause Je - sus is liv - ing for me.
face I shall see, O how I praise Him—He's com-ing for me.

70 SUNRISE

W. C. Poole

B. D. Ackley

Solo

1. When I shall come to the end of my way, When I shall rest at the
2. When in His beau-ty I see the great King, Join with the ran-somed His
3. When life is o - ver and day-light is passed, In heav-en's har - bor my

close of life's day, When "Wel-come home" I shall hear Je - sus say, O
prais - es to sing, When I shall join them my trib - utes to bring, O
an - chor is cast, When I see Je - sus my Sav - ior at last, O

Chorus

that will be sun-rise for me. . . . . Sun-rise to-mor-row, sun-rise to-

mor-row, Sun-rise in glo - ry is wait-ing for me; Sun-rise to-mor-row,

sun-rise to-mor-row, Sun-rise with Je-sus for e - ter - ni - ty.

71 WON'T YOU COME BACK HOME?

James Rowe

De Loss Smith

1. Soul a-stray in dark-ness, bowed by sin and woe, One still dear-ly loves you,
2. Tho' from Him you wan-der, un-der sin's con-trol, Ev-er He is yearn-ing
3. Think how He has suf-fered just to prove His love; E-ven now a man-sion
4. Swift the day is speed-ing; night is com-ing on; Turn, while Je-sus calls you,

tho' you down-ward go; Ten-der-ly He calls you in the gath'ring gloom,
for your way-ward soul; Arms of love are o-pen, Why, de-spair-ing, roam
He pre-pares a-bove, E-ven while you wan-der on to end-less doom:
hope will soon be gone; In the path be-fore you lies a yawn-ing tomb:

REFRAIN

Hear Him sweetly plead-ing: "Won't you come back home?"
From the One who loves you, "Won't you come back home?" Won't you come to Je-sus,
Won't you try to love Him, "Won't you come back home?"
Won't you love the Sav-ior, "Won't you come back home?"

won't you come back home? Still He dearly loves you and is pleading, "Come;" Grieve His heart no

lon-ger, cease from Him to roam, All shall be for-giv-en, "Won't you come back home?"

8

IN THE UPPER GARDEN

C. Austin Miles

C. Austin Miles

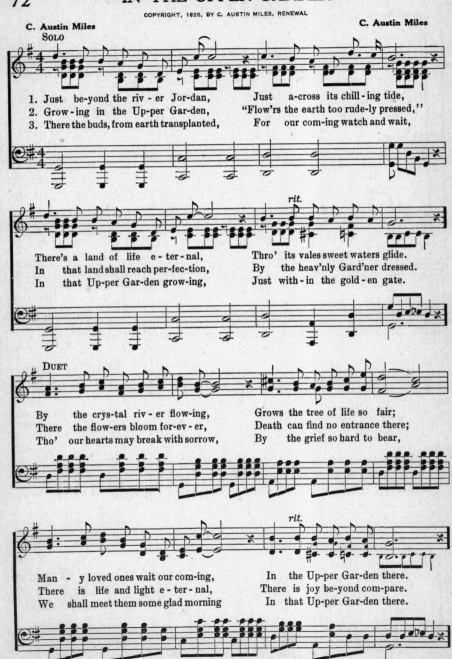

SOLO

1. Just be-yond the riv-er Jor-dan, Just a-cross its chill-ing tide,
2. Grow-ing in the Up-per Gar-den, "Flow'rs the earth too rude-ly pressed,"
3. There the buds, from earth transplanted, For our com-ing watch and wait,

There's a land of life e-ter-nal, Thro' its vales sweet waters glide.
In that land shall reach per-fec-tion, By the heav'nly Gard'ner dressed.
In that Up-per Gar-den grow-ing, Just with-in the gold-en gate.

DUET

By the crys-tal riv-er flow-ing, Grows the tree of life so fair;
There the flow-ers bloom for-ev-er, Death can find no entrance there;
Tho' our hearts may break with sorrow, By the grief so hard to bear,

Man-y loved ones wait our com-ing, In the Up-per Gar-den there.
There is life and light e-ter-nal, There is joy be-yond com-pare.
We shall meet them some glad morning In that Up-per Gar-den there.

IN THE UPPER GARDEN

CHORUS

We shall meet them some bright morn-ing,
We shall meet them some bright morn-ing, some bright morning,
Rest - ing
Rest-ing by

by the wa-ters fair;................
the wa-ters fair, the wa-ters fair;
They are wait-ing for our
They are wait - ing for our

com-ing,
com-ing, for our com-ing,
In the Up-per Gar-den there.
In the Up-per Gar-den, in the Up-per Gar-den there.

Gar - den there.

73 DEAR LORD, FORGIVE

Charles H. Gabriel
SOLO OR QUARTET

COPYRIGHT, 1930, BY HOMER A. RODEHEAVER
INTERNATIONAL COPYRIGHT SECURED

Charles H. Gabriel

1. What have I done for Thee this day, As I have traveled down life's way?
2. Have I by word, or act, or deed Com-fort-ed some-one in their need?
3. Where I have failed Thy will to live, In Thy com-pas-sion, Lord, for-give!

Have I been true in heart and mind, Pa-tient, and wise, and kind?
Have I been faith-ful to my trust, Gen-tle through all, and just?
Fill me with grace to try a-gain; This is my prayer. A-men.

74 WHY NOT ACCEPT HIM NOW?

Grady C. Morris　　　　　　　　　　　　　　　　　　　　　**Grady C. Morris**

1. The hand of the Bless-ed Re-deem - er Is reach-ing to all who are lost;
2. Such love fills the mind with a-maze-ment! Such love nev-er mortal hath shown!
3. No oth - er can save you and lead you To man-sions of glo-ry a - bove;

He of-fers sal-va-tion and par - don, Re-mem-ber-ing nev - er the cost.
He left His bright throne and His glo-ry, That love for the sin - ner be known!
No oth - er could keep and up-hold you By mer - cy and won-der - ful love.

He purchased re-demp-tion for sin - ners, While thorns were up-on His brow!
And now with your soul He is plead - ing, O come, and be-fore Him bow;
Don't wait till the shadows are fall - ing, And death shall make cold the brow;

Re-pent! O be-lieve and re-ceive Him, Soul, why not ac - cept Him now?
He of - fers you full-est sal-va - tion, O why not ac-cept Him now?
To - day is the day of sal-va - tion, O why not ac-cept Him now?

Chorus

The shadows already are fall - ing, Life swiftly is passing a-way! . . .
　　　　　fall-ing like dew;　　　　　　　　　　　　is pass-ing a-way!

WHY NOT ACCEPT HIM NOW?

The voice of "The Master" still call - ing; Come now and be saved to-day. . . .
call-ing to you;   to-day.

75   SINCE HIS LOVE FOUND ME

D. Lauck Currens   Henry P. Morton

1. When in paths of sin I wan-dered, Je-sus came my soul to save;
2. Je - sus sought me when in dark-ness, I was lost in deep de-spair;
3. Have you heard the voice of Je - sus, Call-ing you from sin-ful ways?

Left His home of heav'n-ly splen-dor, And for me His life He gave.
He has filled my life with sun-light, In His glo - ry I shall share.
He will give you peace and par - don, With a song of end-less praise.

CHORUS

Since His love found me, In my heart there rings a mel - o - dy;
found me, my heart

Since His love found me, I have joy and lib - er - ty.
found me, have joy and lib-er-ty.

AT THE END OF THE WAY

76

Rev. W. C. Poole

B. D. Ackley

1. At the end of the way, At the close of the day, At the end of the path-way I roam; With my la - bor all done And the vic - to - ry won, Christ is wait - ing to wel - come me home.

2. At the end of the way, When the mists roll a - way, And the bur - dens of earth are laid down; We shall join the re - frain With our loved ones a - gain, Where the cross will be changed for the crown.

3. I shall meet with the King, And His prais - es will sing Thro' the years of e - ter - ni - ty's day; Thro' His won - der - ful grace I shall look on His face, At the end, at the end of the way.

CHORUS

At the end of the way I will lay my burdens down, At the end of the day I'll re-ceive the promised crown, At the end of the way, at the

AT THE END OF THE WAY

clos-ing of the day, I'll see Je-sus at the end of the way.

of the way.

77   I DO, DON'T YOU?

Melville W. Miller

E. O. Excell

1. I know a great Sav-ior, I do; don't you? I live by His
2. I need Him to lead me, I do; don't you? Heav'n's man-na to
3. I love to be near Him, I do; don't you? He speaks and I
4. I want Him to use me, I do; don't you? For serv-ice to

fa-vor, I do; don't you? For grace I im-plore Him, I
feed me, I do; don't you? What-ev-er be-tide me, I
hear Him, I do; don't you? For me He is car-ing, The
choose me, I do; don't you? I want Him to bless me, To

wor-ship be-fore Him, I love and a-dore Him, I do; don't you?
need Him be-side me, In mer-cy to hide me, I do; don't you?
cross I am bear-ing, I love Him for shar-ing, I do; don't you?
own and con-fess me, Com-plete-ly pos-sess me, I do; don't you?

DOWN FROM HIS GLORY

William E. Booth-Clibborn   Arr. from E. di Capua

1. Down from His glo-ry, Ev - er liv-ing sto - ry, My God and Sav-ior came,
2. What con-de-scen-sion, Bringing us re-demp-tion; That in the dead of night,
3. With-out re-luc-tance, Flesh and blood His substance, He took the form of man,

And Je-sus was His name. Born in a man-ger, To His own a stran-ger,
Not one faint hope in sight, God, gracious, ten-der, Laid a-side His splen-dor,
Revealed the hid-den plan. O glo-rious mys-t'ry, Sac-ri-fice of Cal-v'ry,

Chorus

A Man of sorrows, tears and ag-o - ny.
Stooping to woo, to win, to save my soul. O how I love Him! How I a-
And now I know Thou wert the great "I Am."

dore Him! My breath, my sun-shine, my all in all! The great Cre-a-tor

Be-came my Sav - ior, And all God's full-ness dwell-eth in Him.

79 RESTING IN HIS LOVE

V. P. Brock.

Blanche Kerr Brock.

1. God has shown His lov-ing face From His throne in heav'n a - bove:
2. When the cares of life op-press, When the sky is dark a - bove;
3. O, if you were nev-er blest, With this peace from heav'n a-bove;

And I've found a rest-ing-place, In the shel-ter of His love.
I can al-ways find a rest, In the shel-ter of His love.
There's for you a won-drous rest, In the shel-ter of His love.

CHORUS

I am rest - ing, rest - ing, Rest-ing,
I am rest-ing, sweetly resting, In the shel-ter of His love, Rest-ing in the

sweet - ly rest-ing in His love; I am rest - ing
shel - ter of His love; rest-ing, sweetly resting in the

in His love, Rest-ing in the shel-ter of His love.
shel-ter of His love, Rest - ing in His love.

Rest - ing rest-ing in His love.

80 THE CHRIST OF THE CROSS

F. C. H.

Frank C. Huston

Slowly, tenderly

1. On Cal - va-ry's brow there was plant-ed a cross, Which lift - ed a
2. They knew not their deeds of that one might-y hour, "O Fa - ther, for-
3. Let oth - ers, who will, praise the cross of the Christ, The Christ of the

Inst.

man up to shame; But He on the cross was the dear Son of God,
give them," He cried; They knew not the cross, long the em - blem of shame,
cross, is my theme; For tho' we must cher-ish the old rug-ged cross,

CHORUS *f*

Who died a lost world to re - claim.
Was there by the Christ glo-ri - fied.
'Tis on - ly the Christ can re - deem.

The Christ of the cross is the

ff

f

theme of my song, The won-der-ful Christ of the cross. He a-tone-ment has

ff

dim. rall.

made; He my ran-som has paid, So I'll praise Him, { The / My } Christ of the cross.

81 MY COUNTRY

A. H. Ackley   A. H. Ackley

1. The call to arms, may it nev-er sound, My coun-try, my
2. Thy jus-tice ech-oes a-round the world, My coun-try, my
3. May God in mer-cy pro-tect thy reign, My coun-try, my

coun-try, But if the foe on thy soil be found, My coun-try, my
coun-try, In man's be-half is thy flag un-furled, My coun-try, my
coun-try, And all u-nite in the proud re-frain, My coun-try, my

coun-try, Let the cow-ards quake be-fore the can-non's roar;
coun-try, But the yoke of slav-er-y we can-not stand,
coun-try; May the love of right-eous-ness our hearts in-spire,

While the blood of pa-tri-ots is flow-ing as of yore, I
We will fight for free-dom at the word of thy com-mand, No
And the com-mon good be ev-'ry hon-est man's de-sire, With

love my life but I love thee more, My coun-try, my coun-try.
ty-rant bold shall pos-sess our land, My coun-try, my coun-try.
love for thee set our hearts on fire, My coun-try, my coun-try.

I WANT TO GO THERE

Words and melody by D. Sullins

Harmony by Prof. Riggs, C. F. College

1. They tell of a cit-y far up in the sky, I want to go
2. When the old ship of Zi-on shall make her last trip, I want to go
3. When Je-sus is crowned the King of all kings, I want to go

there, I do; 'Tis built in the land of "the sweet by and by,"
there, I do; With heads all un-cov-ered to greet the old ship,
there, I do; With shout-ing and clap-ping till all heav-en rings,

I want to go there, don't you? There Je-sus has gone to pre-
I want to go there, don't you? When all the ship's com-pa-ny
I want to go there, don't you? We'll shout hal-le-lu-jah a-

pare us all homes, I want to go there, I do; Where sick-ness nor
meet on the strand, I want to go there, I do; With songs on their
gain and a-gain— I want to go there, I do— And close with the

sor-row nor death ev-er comes, I want to go there, don't you?
lips and with harps in their hands, I want to go there, don't you?
cho-rus, *A-men and A-men,*— I want to go there, don't you?

MY GUIDE AND FRIEND

Charles H. Gabriel

Charles H. Gabriel

Duet

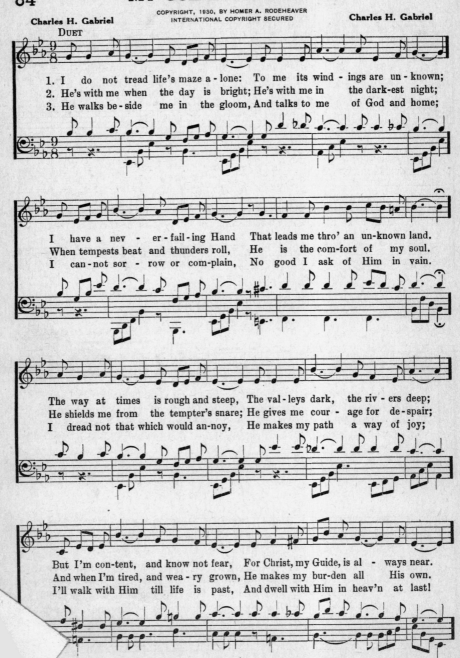

1. I do not tread life's maze a-lone: To me its wind-ings are un-known;
2. He's with me when the day is bright; He's with me in the dark-est night;
3. He walks be-side me in the gloom, And talks to me of God and home;

I have a nev-er-fail-ing Hand That leads me thro' an un-known land.
When tempests beat and thunders roll, He is the com-fort of my soul.
I can-not sor-row or com-plain, No good I ask of Him in vain.

The way at times is rough and steep, The val-leys dark, the riv-ers deep;
He shields me from the tempter's snare; He gives me cour-age for de-spair;
I dread not that which would an-noy, He makes my path a way of joy;

But I'm con-tent, and know not fear, For Christ, my Guide, is al-ways near.
And when I'm tired, and wea-ry grown, He makes my bur-den all His own.
I'll walk with Him till life is past, And dwell with Him in heav'n at last!

MY GUIDE AND FRIEND

REFRAIN.

He is my Comfort, Guide and Friend, Whose precious bless-ings nev-er end;

He is my Com - fort, Guide and Friend, Whose precious blessings never end;

f   *rit. e dim.*

He knows my weak-ness, knows my need; He is the Friend of friends in-deed.

85 NOT MY OWN WILL, LORD

COPYRIGHT, 1930, BY MRS. F. W. SUFFIELD

Frederick W. Suffield   Mrs. F. W. Suffield

1. Not my own will, Lord, this I can say, Not for one mo-ment to have my way;
2. Thou hast a plan, Lord, for me each day, Some work to do, Lord, some word to say;
3. Thou hast a place, Lord, for me to fill, Where I can know, Lord, and do Thy will;
4. Thou hast a work, Lord, for me to do, Out in the high-way, or with the few,

Thy plan is best, Lord, this now I know, Lead where thou wilt, Lord, I'll gladly go.
Make Thy will known now, make my path plain, I'll go with Thee, Lord, come loss or gain.
No choice have I, Lord, where it shall be, Home or a-broad, Lord, on land or sea.
A word to com-fort, a heart that's drear, A song to glad-den, a smile to cheer.

THE LOVE OF CHRIST

86

Chas. H. Gabriel
Chas. H. Gabriel

DUET. *Soprano and Tenor* HOMER A. RODEHEAVER, OWNER

1. Ere   I knew the blessed fullness of The love of Christ, the Man of Gal-i-lee,
2. I   was wand'ring in the des-ert, lost, When first I saw Him beckon from a-far,
3. Doubting, trembling, hoping, mocked by fear, At last I caught the beauty of His face,
4. Sweet-er than the mu-sic of the stars, As they to-geth-er sang at birth, will be

With-in my soul I felt its lat-ent pow'r Like wa-ters flowing o-ver me.
And as He raised His blessed hand to me, I saw that cru-el, crim-son scar.
And as I cried a-loud to Him, that hour He saved me by His wondrous grace.
The bless-ed name of Je-sus to my soul, Thro' time and in e-ter-ni-ty.

CHORUS

The love that once   I   despised, re-ject-ed,   Is far be-
The love that once   I   de-spised, re-ject-ed, Is...

yond   all   I had ex-pect-ed; O, that I had not   so long neg-
far be-yond all I had ex-pect-ed;   O, that I had   not

THE LOVE OF CHRIST

lect - ed .... The One who died for me on Cal-va-ry.
so long neg-lect-ed The One who died for me on Cal-va-ry.

87   HOW CAN I HELP BUT LOVE HIM?

Elton M. Roth

Elton M. Roth

1. Down from His splen-dor in glo-ry He came, In-to a world of woe;
2. I   am un-wor-thy to take of His grace, Won-der-ful grace so free;
3. He   is the fair-est of thou-sands to me, His love is sweet and true;

Took on Him-self all my guilt and my shame, Why should He love me so?
Yet Je-sus suf-fered and died in my place, E'en for a soul like me.
Won-der-ful beau-ty in Him I now see, More than I ev-er knew.

CHORUS

How can I help but love Him, When He loved me so?

Slower

How can I help but love Him, When He loved me so?

88 LORD, HOLD MY HAND

Rev. R. H. McDaniel

B. D. Ackley

DUET. *Not too fast*

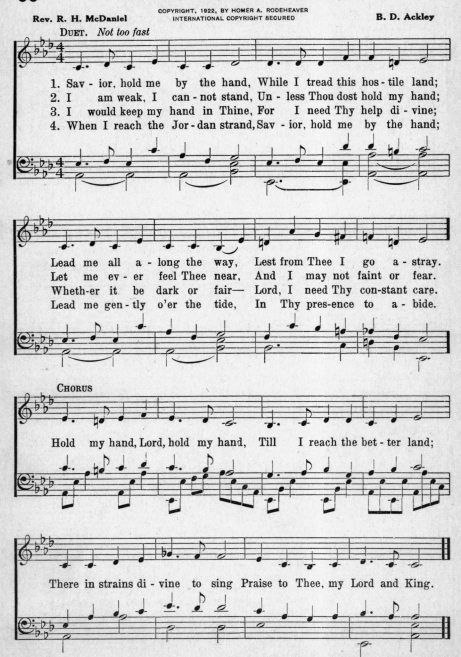

1. Sav - ior, hold me by the hand, While I tread this hos - tile land;
2. I am weak, I can - not stand, Un - less Thou dost hold my hand;
3. I would keep my hand in Thine, For I need Thy help di - vine;
4. When I reach the Jor - dan strand, Sav - ior, hold me by the hand;

Lead me all a - long the way, Lest from Thee I go a - stray.
Let me ev - er feel Thee near, And I may not faint or fear.
Wheth-er it be dark or fair— Lord, I need Thy con-stant care.
Lead me gen - tly o'er the tide, In Thy pres-ence to a - bide.

CHORUS

Hold my hand, Lord, hold my hand, Till I reach the bet - ter land;

There in strains di - vine to sing Praise to Thee, my Lord and King.

89 HE'LL NEVER FORGET TO KEEP ME

"Yes, I have loved thee with an everlasting love."—Jer. 31: 3.   "For I am the Lord, I change not."—Mal. 3: 6

F. A. Graves   F. A. Graves

Duet. *Tenor and Alto*

1. My Fa - ther has man-y dear chil - dren; Will He ev-er   for-get to keep me?
2. Our Fa - ther re-mem-bers the spar-rows, Their val - ue   and fall He doth see;
3. The words of the Lord are so price - less, How pa-tient   and watch-ful is He;
4. I now will a - bide in His shad - ow, Nev-er rest-less   nor fear-ful will be;
5. O broth-er, why don't you ac-cept Him? He   of-fers   sal-va - tion so free;

He   gave His own Son to re-deem them, And He can-not for-get to keep me.
But dear-er to   Him are His chil-dren, And He'll nev-er for-get to keep me.
Tho' moth-er for - get her own off-spring, Yet He'll nev-er for-get to keep me.
In the se - cret of His presence He'll hide me, And He'll nev-er for-get to keep me.
Re - pent and be - lieve and o-bey Him, And He'll nev-er for-get to keep thee.

REFRAIN

1-4. He'll nev-er for-get to keep me (keep me), He'll nev-er for-get to keep me (keep me);
5. He'll nev-er for-get to keep thee (keep thee), He'll nev-er for-get to keep thee (keep thee);

1 He   gave His own Son to re-deem me, And He'll nev-er for-get to keep me.
2 But dear - er to   Him are His chil-dren, And He'll nev-er for-get to keep me.
3 Tho' moth-er for - get her own offspring, Yet He'll nev-er for-get to keep me.
   In the se-cret of His presence He'll hide me, And He'll nev-er for-get to keep me.
   Re - pent and be - lieve and o-bey Him, And He'll nev-er for-get to keep thee.

JESUS OF NAZARETH

Chas. H. Gabriel   **Chas. H. Gabriel**

1. I stood in the gar-den of Geth-sem-a-ne, Whose a-ges-old
2. He prayed in the si-lence that hal-lowed the place, And lo! drops of
3. A-gain on the cross where He suf-fered and died, Blasphemed by the

ol-ive trees whis-pered to me; When One I saw en-ter its
blood kissed His ag-o-nized face! "Not my will, but Thine be done!"
rab-ble, de-sert-ed, de-nied; I hear Him still pray-ing, and

shad-ows a-lone, And heard His heart-bro-ken ap-peal to the throne.
Who could it be, In sor-row and grief in-ter-ced-ing for me?
know it was I For whom He, my Lord, con-de-scend-ed to die!

CHORUS

'Twas Je-sus of Naz-a-reth, Mas-ter di-vine! My bless-ed Re-

deem-er, my Sav-ior and thine! Neg-lect-ed, de-sert-ed, for-

got-ten in shame, A-lone to the gar-den at mid-night He came.

91   I WANT TO LIVE HIS LOVE TO SHOW

Geo. Bennard   WORDS AND MUSIC COPYRIGHT, 1927, BY GEO. BENNARD   Rev. Geo. Bennard

DUET

1. I   sing of Him whom angels praise, And seraphs glad   ho-san-nas raise,
2. The life He lived   cre-ates in me   A   deep de-sire   like Him to be;
3. 'Twas not His life   and that a-lone   That did for hu-man guilt a-tone,
4. His life, His death, His emp-ty grave, Proclaim His love, His pow'r to save;

Of Him who walked with sin-ful men   And lived and died   with-out a stain.
And when I think   of how He died   I   long that self   be cru-ci-fied.
But when up-on   the cru-el tree   He bled and died   for you and me.
And when He comes to claim His own   He'll sit as Judge up-on the throne.

REFRAIN

To Him who gave Him-self for me   I give my life, tho' poor it be;

And here, and ev-'ry-where I go,   I want to live   His love to show.

LOVE DIVINE

To my friend, O. L. Cotterell

Gerald E. Bonney
DUET

Gerald E. Bonney

1. It was love that sent a Sav - ior To this world of sin and woe;
2. It was love that heard my pleadings When I cried out in my sin;
3. It is love that still is knock-ing At the hearts of sin - ful men;

It was love that left heav'n's por-tals, And came down to dwell be - low;
It was love that gave me com - fort; It was love that took me in;
It is love that nev - er ti - res, But that knocks and knocks a - gain;

It was love that stilled the wa - ters On the storm-y Gal - i - lee;
It was love that whis-pered soft - ly, "I will nev - er cast you out;"
It is love that solves all prob-lems In this world of care and strife;

It was love that paid sin's ran - som, One dark day on Cal - va - ry.
It was love that eased my heart-ache; It was love re-moved my doubt.
It is love, the love of Je - sus, That gives hope, and peace, and life.

LOVE DIVINE

Chorus

Love so di - vine, love so sub - lime, Love that is deep - er than

an - y sea; Love for us all, O how can it be!

93 IN JESUS

A. M. Robert Harkness

Duet. *Slowly*

1. I've tried in vain a thou-sand ways My fears to quell, my hopes to
2. My soul is night, my heart is steel, I can-not see, I can-not
3. He died, He lives, He reigns, He pleads; There's love in all His words and
4. Tho' some should sneer, and some should blame, I'll go with all my guilt and

raise; But what I need, the Bi - ble says, Is ev - er, on - ly Je - sus.
feel: For light, for life, I must ap - peal In sim-ple faith to Je - sus.
deeds; There's all a guilt - y sin - ner needs For-ev - er-more in Je - sus.
shame; I'll go to Him be-cause His name, A-bove all names, is Je - sus.

THE CHURCH OF LONG AGO

TUNE—"When You and I Were Young, Maggie"

S. S. Lappin

J. A. Butterfield

Moderato mf

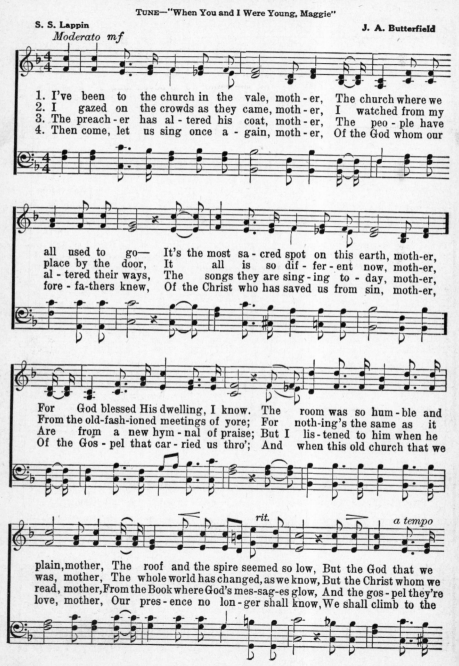

1. I've been to the church in the vale, moth-er, The church where we
2. I gazed on the crowds as they came, moth-er, I watched from my
3. The preach-er has al-tered his coat, moth-er, The peo-ple have
4. Then come, let us sing once a-gain, moth-er, Of the God whom our

all used to go— It's the most sa-cred spot on this earth, moth-er,
place by the door, It all is so dif-fer-ent now, moth-er,
al-tered their ways, The songs they are sing-ing to-day, moth-er,
fore-fa-thers knew, Of the Christ who has saved us from sin, moth-er,

For God blessed His dwelling, I know. The room was so hum-ble and
From the old-fash-ioned meetings of yore; For noth-ing's the same as it
Are from a new hym-nal of praise; But I lis-tened to him when he
Of the Gos-pel that car-ried us thro'; And when this old church that we

rit.   a tempo

plain, mother, The roof and the spire seemed so low, But the God that we
was, mother, The whole world has changed, as we know, But the Christ whom we
read, mother, From the Book where God's mes-sag-es glow, And the gos-pel they're
love, mother, Our pres-ence no lon-ger shall know, We shall climb to the

THE CHURCH OF LONG AGO

wor-ship to-day, moth-er, Is the God that we loved long a - go.
hon - or to - day, moth-er, Is the Christ of the long, long a - go.
preaching to-day, moth-er, Is the same we o-beyed long a - go.
man-sions a - bove, moth-er, From the Church of the long, long a - go.

95 GRACE IS FLOWING FOR ME

Lizzie DeArmond

COPYRIGHT, 1930, BY HOMER A. RODEHEAVER
INTERNATIONAL COPYRIGHT SECURED

James C. Moore

1. God's grace like a riv - er is flow - ing, The life-tide from lone Cal - va -
2. It leads to the cross as a ref - uge, Its cleansing flood ev - er is
3. God's grace, precious gift with-out meas-ure, O'er sin helped me gain vic - to -

ry; 'Tis won - der - ful I am re-deemed by His grace, The
free; I'll praise Him for - ev - er, who sent in His love The
ry; "All glo - ry to Him," with re - joic - ing I sing, For

CHORUS

grace that is flow-ing for me. Grace, grace is flowing for me; Grace, grace is

flow-ing for me; Won-der-ful, marvelous, flowing for me From Cal-va - ry.

96 HE'S NEAR, YES, EVER NEAR

Gerald E. Bonney

Gerald E. Bonney

DUET

1. I have a Friend who un-der-stands, He's near, yes, ev-er near; He knows my
2. I have a Guide who knows the way, He's near, yes, ev-er near; He marks my
3. I have a Shep-herd, kind and true, He's near, yes, ev-er near; He guards His
4. I have a Sav-ior up a-bove, He's near, yes, ev-er near; He tells me

hopes, He knows my plans, He's near, yes, ev-er near; Whene'er I'm tired He gives me
path from day to day, He's near, yes, ev-er near; Whene'er the day is dark as
sheep the long day thro', He's near, yes, ev-er near; Whene'er I wan-der from the
dai - ly of His love, He's near, yes, ev-er near; Whene'er I think of Cal - va-

rest, If I but come at His re - quest And lay my head up - on His
night He floods the path with His own light, And then I know the way is
fold, Out on the mountains, bleak and cold, He brings me back with love un-
ry, I know He gave His life for me, And that some day His face I'll

REFRAIN

breast; He's near, yes, ev-er near. He's near, so near, He's near, yes, ev-er
right; He's near, yes, ev-er near. He's near, so near, He's near, yes, ev-er
told; He's near, yes, ev-er near. He's near, so near, He's near, yes, ev-er
see; He's near, yes, ev-er near. He's near, so near, He's near, yes, ev-er

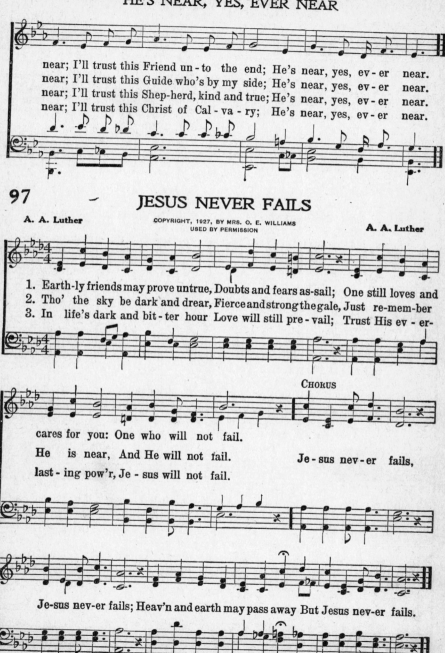

near; I'll trust this Friend un-to the end; He's near, yes, ev-er near.
near; I'll trust this Guide who's by my side; He's near, yes, ev-er near.
near; I'll trust this Shep-herd, kind and true; He's near, yes, ev-er near.
near; I'll trust this Christ of Cal-va-ry; He's near, yes, ev-er near.

97 — **JESUS NEVER FAILS**

A. A. Luther

A. A. Luther

1. Earth-ly friends may prove untrue, Doubts and fears as-sail; One still loves and
2. Tho' the sky be dark and drear, Fierce and strong the gale, Just re-mem-ber
3. In life's dark and bit-ter hour Love will still pre-vail; Trust His ev-er-

CHORUS

cares for you: One who will not fail.

He is near, And He will not fail.

last-ing pow'r, Je-sus will not fail.

Je-sus nev-er fails,

Je-sus nev-er fails; Heav'n and earth may pass away But Jesus nev-er fails.

98 SINCE MY LIFE IS HID AWAY WITH CHRIST IN GOD

George W. Cooke

F. W. Seiler

1. I am think-ing day by day Of the past so far a-way, Since my
2. No more dead in sin and loss, Safe-ly liv-ing 'neath the Cross, Since my
3. Now with Christ who is my life, Lead-ing thro' this earth-ly strife, Since my
4. To be ris-en with the Lord, Know the beau-ty of His Word, Since my

life is hid a-way with Christ in God; How He lis-tened to my cry,
life is hid a-way with Christ in God; All to Him I free-ly bring,
life is hid a-way with Christ in God; No more doubt nor stain of sin,
life is hid a-way with Christ in God; "All His prom-is-es are sure,"

And with saving grace drew nigh, Since my life is hid a-way with Christ in God.
He is Prophet, Priest and King, Since my life is hid a-way with Christ in God.
With His righteousness with-in, Since my life is hid a-way with Christ in God.
For His grace it must en-dure, Since my life is hid a-way with Christ in God.

CHORUS

Since my life is hid a-way with Christ in God, Since my life is hid a-

way with Christ in God, I am hap-py night and day, I have

SINCE MY LIFE IS HID AWAY WITH CHRIST IN GOD

vic-t'ry all the way, Since my life is hid a-way with Christ in God.

99 IN THE JUDGMENT DAY

A. H. Ackley

A. H. Ackley

1. What will you do when the judg-ment day Shall try your soul?
2. You will re-call ev-'ry act of wrong That you have done,
3. All se-cret mo-tives shall be made plain, And ev-'ry thought,

When the Great Judge of the world shall say, "Bring forth the scroll"?
And how you failed, when your strength was strong, Some help-less one;
Can-not be hid-den the guilt-y stain That sin has wrought;

And from the record your deeds shall be read, Deeds you have long since forgotten as dead,
Un-der the gaze of God's all-seeing eye, You will be judged for your life by and by,
Thus shall Christ speak, and His judgments are true, "From Me depart, I have never known you."

What will you do, O, what will you say, How will you stand in the judgment day?

100 SATISFIED THERE

E. E. Hewitt

B. D. Ackley

1. I'll trust the dear Fa-ther who knows what is best, The cross He will
2. He'll show me the mean-ing of ev-'ry dark day, Of seem-ing de-
3. I know not what won-der-ful joys shall be mine, When clad in His
4. I know not the form of the friends I shall greet, When called in their

help me to bear; In yonder bright home there remaineth a rest, And
ni-al to pray'r; I'll see that His love free-ly brightened the way, And
beau-ty so fair, There, fadeless, for-ev-er, His glo-ry will shine, And
rap-ture to share, But when at the feet of the Mas-ter we meet, I

REFRAIN.

I shall be sat-is-fied there......
I shall be sat-is-fied there., ... Yes, I shall be sat-is-fied
I shall be sat-is-fied there.......
know we'll be sat-is-fied there.......
sat-is-fied there.

there,.... I shall be sat-is-fied there;.... In realms ev-er
sat-is-fied there,   sat-is-fied there;

blest there re-main-eth a rest, And I shall be sat-is-fied there.....
sat-is-fied there.

101 PAUSE FOR A MOMENT OF PRAYER

"Men ought always to pray and not to faint" Luke 18:1

Ina Duley Ogdon

Joseph S. Waugh

DUET. *Alto and Tenor*

1. Wea - ry and worn in the bat - tle of life, Driv - en and beat-en by
2. Pray for His strength lest you fall by the way; Plead for His grace to sus-
3. Pause to par - take of the sweet liv-ing bread; Drink of His life at the

sor - row and strife, Turn to your Sav - ior your bur - den to share,
tain you to - day; Safe - ly through e - vil His ar - mor to wear,
great foun-tain head; Christ will re - store you from sin and de - spair,

CHORUS

Pause at His feet for a mo-ment of prayer. Pause at His feet for a

mo-ment of prayer, Hon-or the dear blessed name that we bear; Pause in your

hur - ry, wor - ry and care, Pause at His feet for a mo-ment of prayer.

102 ERE THE SUN GOES DOWN

Chas. H. Gabriel   Chas. H. Gabriel

1. There is work that I must do ere the sun goes down—
2. I've been led o'er man-y fields fraught with ur-gent need,
3. I re-pent the rec-ord, Lord, though the hour is late,

Some-thing that will add a gem to my fade-less crown; Lord, I
I have heard the voice di-vine with my con-science plead, But have
And would seek the works of love that for me a-wait; Take a-

know not where it lies, what the task may be, But I know Thou wilt re-
failed in man-y tasks that were mine to do—To my vows un-faith-ful
way Thy judgment, Lord, from the crim-son past, And re-ceive me to Thy-

CHORUS

veal Thy de-sire in me.
been, and to God un-true.   Ere the sun goes down, ere the sun goes down!
self safe in heav'n at last.

I have work re-main-ing, scarce be-gun;   Ere the sun goes down,
ere the sun goes down;

ERE THE SUN GOES DOWN

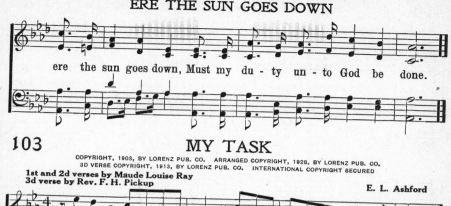

ere the sun goes down, Must my du - ty un - to God be done.

103   MY TASK

1st and 2d verses by Maude Louise Ray
3d verse by Rev. F. H. Pickup

E. L. Ashford

Intro. f   p

1. To love some-one more dear-ly ev - 'ry day, . . . To help a wan-d'ring
2. To fol-low truth as blind men long for light, . . . To do my best from
3. And then my Sav - ior by and by to meet, . . . When faith hath made her

child to find his way,   To pon-der o'er a no - ble tho't and pray,
dawn of day till night,   To keep my heart fit for His ho - ly sight,
task on earth com-plete,   And lay my hom-age at the Mas-ter's feet,

And smile when evening falls, And smile when evening falls, This is my task.
And an-swer when He calls, And answer when He calls, This is my task.
With - in the jas - per walls, With-in the jas - per walls, This crowns my task.

104 IT PAYS TO SERVE JESUS

Frank C. Huston

Frank C. Huston

DUET

1. The serv-ice of Je-sus true pleas-ure af-fords, In Him there is joy with-out an al-loy; 'Tis heav-en to trust Him and rest on His words; It pays to serve Je-sus each day.

2. It pays to serve Je-sus what-e'er may be-tide, It pays to be true what-e'er you may do; 'Tis rich-es of mer-cy in Him to a-bide; It pays to serve Je-sus each day.

3. Tho' sometimes the shad-ows may hang o'er the way, And sor-rows may come to beck-on us home, Our pre-cious Re-deem-er each toil will re-pay; It pays to serve Je-sus each day.

CHORUS

It pays to serve Je-sus, it pays ev-'ry day, It pays ev-'ry step of the way; . . . Tho' the pathway to glo-ry may sometimes be drear, You'll be hap-py each step of the way.

105 THE BLESSED OLD STORY IS TRUE

Frederick W. Suffield

Mrs. F. W. Suffield

DUET. *Soprano and Alto*

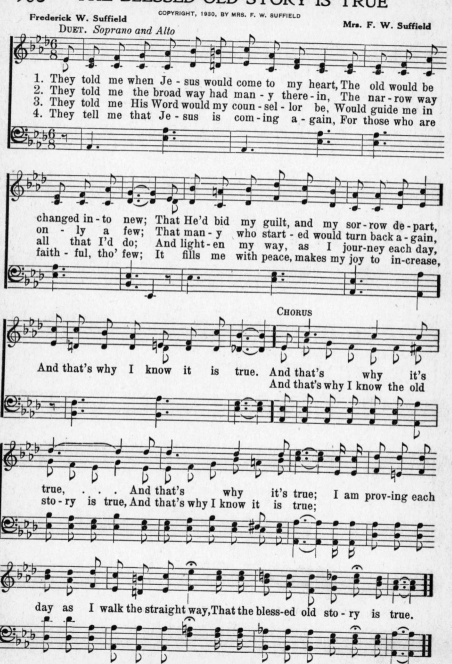

1. They told me when Je-sus would come to my heart, The old would be changed in-to new; That He'd bid my guilt, and my sor-row de-part,
2. They told me the broad way had man-y there-in, The nar-row way on-ly a few; That man-y who start-ed would turn back a-gain,
3. They told me His Word would my coun-sel-lor be, Would guide me in all that I'd do; And light-en my way, as I jour-ney each day,
4. They tell me that Je-sus is com-ing a-gain, For those who are faith-ful, tho' few; It fills me with peace, makes my joy to in-crease,

CHORUS

And that's why I know it is true. And that's why it's true, . . . And that's why it's true; I am prov-ing each
And that's why I know the old sto-ry is true, And that's why I know it is true;

day as I walk the straight way, That the bless-ed old sto-ry is true.

106 THE BROKEN-HEARTED SAVIOR

Rev. T. V. Voorhees

Carl Blackmore

1. My heart o'er-flows with a sto - ry Of Je - sus, my
2. I   fear to - day, as I   won - der How time up - on
3. O   friend, now Je - sus be heed - ing, No lon - ger His

Sav - ior and King; I'll tell it till tak - en to Glo - ry,
time I said "No;" How I tore His heart-strings a - sun - der,
shed blood de - ny; Just list to His pas - sion - ate plead - ing,

And this is the mes-sage I'll bring:
And there made His life's blood to flow.
And make this your heart-search-ing cry.

CHORUS

Bro - ken-heart - ed my
Sav - ior died, Bro - ken-heart - ed to set me free; There cru - ci-
fied, re - viled, de - nied; Bro - ken-heart - ed, He died for me.

107 I'M NOT ALONE

COPYRIGHT, 1912, BY THE PRAISE PUB. CO.
HOMER A. RODEHEAVER, OWNER

Rev. W. C. Poole

Wm. Edie Marks

DUET

1. How sweet the tho't that comes to me On moun-tain or on storm-y sea,
2. When sin would lead my feet a-stray, My Shep-herd holds me all the way;
3. When pressed my soul in thick-est fight, He helps me in the cause of right;
4. While oth-ers lone-ly are and sad, My Sav-ior's presence makes me glad,

There is no land, or clime, or zone, Where Je-sus leaves His sheep a-lone.
En-tic-ing snares a-round me thrown, He leads safe past; I'm not a-lone.
The foes so strong, by Him are known; I'm not a-lone, I'm not a-lone.
He knows my heart; I am His own; I'm not a-lone, I'm not a-lone.

QUARTET OR CHORUS

Let all the things I've loved and known Like leaves be-
Let all the things I've loved and known Like

fore the wind be blown, My Sav-ior lives,
leaves be-fore the wind be blown, My Sav-ior lives,

ritard.

I am His own, I'm not a-lone! I'm not a-lone!
I am His own,

108 THE BIRD WITH A BROKEN WING

Dedicated to Thomas Elgar

Copyright, 1890, by F. M. Lamb
Used by permission

HEZEKIAH BUTTERWORTH

F. M. LAMB

1. I walked thro' the woodland mead-ows, Where sweet the thrushes sing;
2. I found a young life bro - ken By sin's se-duc-tive art;
3. But the bird with a bro - ken pin - ion Kept an-oth - er from the snare;

And found on a bed of moss-es, A bird with a bro-ken wing.
And touch'd with a Christ-like pit - y I took him to my heart.
And the life that sin had strick - en Rais'd an - oth - er from de - spair.

I healed its wound, and each morn-ing It sang its old sweet strain;
He lived with a no - ble pur - pose, And strug-gled not in vain;
For Christ, the might - y Heal - er, Has a balm for ev - 'ry pain;

But the bird with a bro - ken pin - ion Nev - er soared so high a - gain.
But the life that sin had strick - en, Nev - er soared so high a - gain.
And the soul that He has heal - ed, High - er still may rise a - gain.

AFTER

Gipsy Simon Smith
SOLO OR DUET

Henry P. Morton

1. Aft - er the tri - als and aft - er the tears, Aft - er the doubting and
2. Aft - er the struggles when all seems so vain, Aft - er the weep-ing and
3. Aft - er the heartache the balm from a - bove, And with the tri - als our

aft - er the fears, Aft - er the dread and the dark-ness of night,
sor - row and pain, Aft - er the an - guish at Geth-sem - a - ne,
God and His love, Aft - er the bur - dens of life we lay down,

REFRAIN

Com - eth the morn-ing all peace-ful and bright. Aft - er the storm
Min - is-t'ring spir - its to wait up - on thee.   storm-clouds
Aft - er the cross then the con-quer-or's crown.

shin-eth the sun; Aft - er temp-ta-tion the vic-to - ry won; Aft - er life's
sun - light;

voy-age when breakers are past, Safe in the heav-en-ly har-bor at last.

110 HE TOUCHED ME AND MADE ME WHOLE

Thomas Sullivan

Thomas Sullivan

1. To the feet of my Sav - ior, in trem - bling and fear, A
2. I knew not the ten - der com - pas - sion and love That
3. "My grace is suf - fi - cient," I heard His dear voice, "O
4. O Je - sus, dear Je - sus, Thy name I a - dore, For
5. O come, my dear broth - er, He's wait - ing for you, Your

pen - i - tent sin - ner I came; He saw, and in mer - cy He
Je - sus, my Sav - ior, had shown; Tho' bur-dened with grief, His dear
come and find rest for your soul; From sin you to save, my life
sav - ing and keep-ing my soul; Thy prais - es I'll sing, my Re-
sin - bur-dened heart to con - sole; Your wea - ry head rest on His

bade me draw near; All glo - ry and praise to His name.
hand brought re - lief; He healed me and called me His own.
free - ly I gave; I died that you might be made whole."
deem - er and King, Thy dear, lov - ing hand made me whole.
dear, lov - ing breast; He suf - fered and died for your soul.

CHORUS

He touched me and thus made me whole (made me whole), Bring-ing

com-fort and rest to my soul (to my soul); O glad hap - py day, all my

HE TOUCHED ME AND MADE ME WHOLE

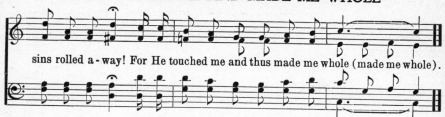

sins rolled a-way! For He touched me and thus made me whole (made me whole).

111   JUST WHERE HE NEEDS ME MOST

COPYRIGHT, 1911, BY CHAS. H. GABRIEL
HOMER A. RODEHEAVER, OWNER

W. C. Poole   Chas. H. Gabriel

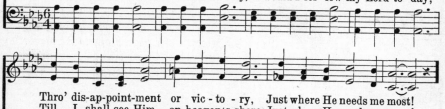

1. Just where He needs me, there would I be, Working for Je-sus who died for me;
2. Just where He needs me! He goes be-fore; Just where He needs me till life is o'er;
3. Just where He needs me by day or night, Just where He needs me, in-to the fight,
4. Just where He needs me! He knows the way, So would I fol-low my Lord to-day;

Thro' dis-ap-point-ment or vic-to-ry, Just where He needs me most!
Till I shall see Him on heaven's shore, Just where He needs me most!
Or wait for or-ders; He leads a-right, Just where He needs me most!
Where Je-sus wants me, there would I stay, Just where He needs me most!

CHORUS

Just where He needs me most,   Just where He needs me most;

His work to do, faith-ful and true, Just where He needs me most.

112 HARK! I HEAR MY NAME

WORDS AND MUSIC COPYRIGHT, 1909, BY P. P. BILHORN
INTERNATIONAL COPYRIGHT SECURED

I. D. O.

B. D. Ackley

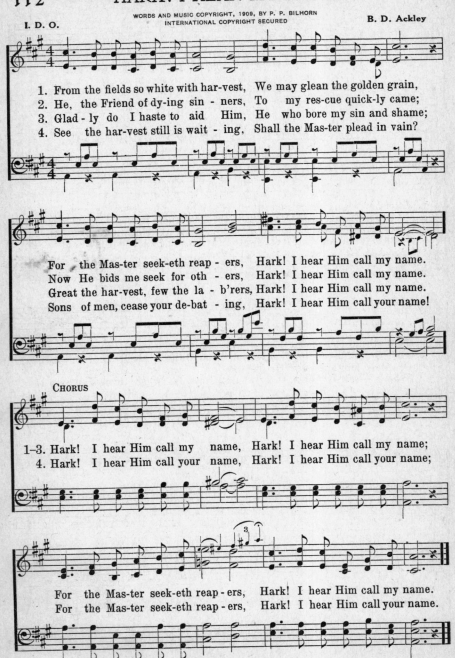

1. From the fields so white with har-vest, We may glean the golden grain,
2. He, the Friend of dy-ing sin - ners, To my res-cue quick-ly came;
3. Glad - ly do I haste to aid Him, He who bore my sin and shame;
4. See the har-vest still is wait - ing, Shall the Mas-ter plead in vain?

For the Mas-ter seek-eth reap - ers, Hark! I hear Him call my name.
Now He bids me seek for oth - ers, Hark! I hear Him call my name.
Great the har-vest, few the la - b'rers, Hark! I hear Him call my name.
Sons of men, cease your de-bat - ing, Hark! I hear Him call your name!

CHORUS

1–3. Hark! I hear Him call my name, Hark! I hear Him call my name;
4. Hark! I hear Him call your name, Hark! I hear Him call your name;

For the Mas-ter seek-eth reap - ers, Hark! I hear Him call my name.
For the Mas-ter seek-eth reap - ers, Hark! I hear Him call your name.

113 SPEAK, MY LORD

George Bennard

COPYRIGHT, 1911, BY GEO. BENNARD

George Bennard

1. Hear the Lord of har-vest sweet-ly call-ing, "Who will go and
2. When the coal of fire . . . touched the proph-et, Mak-ing him as
3. Mil-lions now in sin and shame are dy-ing; Lis-ten to their
4. Soon the time for reap-ing will be o-ver; Soon we'll gath-er

work for Me to-day? Who will bring to Me the lost and dy-ing?
pure, as pure can be; When the voice of God said,"Who'll go for us?"
sad and bit-ter cry; Has-ten, broth-er, has-ten to the res-cue;
for the har-vest-home; May the Lord of har-vest smile up-on us,

CHORUS

Who will point them to the nar-row way?"
Then he answered,"Here I am, send me." Speak, my Lord, speak, my
Quick-ly an-swer,"Mas-ter, here am I."
May we hear His bless-ed,"Child, well done." Speak, my Lord,

Lord, Speak, and I'll be quick to an-swer Thee; Speak, my
speak, my Lord, to answer Thee;

rit.

Lord, speak, my Lord, Speak, and I will answer,"Lord, send me."
Speak, my Lord, "Lord, send me."

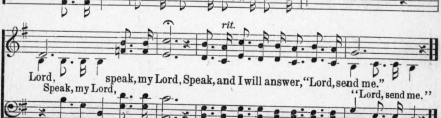

114 OVER THE LINE

Ellen K. Bradford

E. H. Phelps

1. O how ten-der and sweet was the Mas-ter's voice, As He
2. But my sins are man-y, my faith is small, Lo! the
3. But my flesh is weak, I tear-ful-ly said, And the
4. Ah, the world is cold, and I can-not go back, Press

lov-ing-ly called to me, "Come o-ver the line, it is
an-swer came quick and clear; "Thou need-est not trust in thy-
way I can-not see; I fear if I try I may
for-ward I sure-ly must; I'll place my hand in His

on-ly a step— I'm wait-ing, my child, for thee."
self at all, Step o-ver the line, I am here."
sad-ly fail, And thus may dis-hon-or Thee.
wound-ed palm, Step o-ver the line, and *trust*.

REFRAIN

"O-ver the line," hear the sweet refrain, Angels are chanting the heavenly strain;

"O-ver the line," Why should I re-main With a step between me and Je-sus?
4th v. "O-ver the line," I *will not* re-main, I will cross it and go to Je-sus.

115 DON'T TURN THE SAVIOR AWAY

Harry D. Clarke

Harry D. Clarke

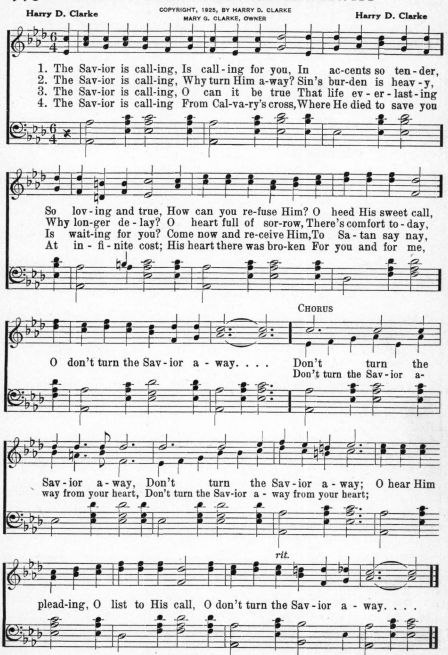

1. The Sav-ior is call-ing, Is call-ing for you, In ac-cents so ten-der,
2. The Sav-ior is call-ing, Why turn Him a-way? Sin's bur-den is heav-y,
3. The Sav-ior is call-ing, O can it be true That life ev-er-last-ing
4. The Sav-ior is call-ing From Cal-va-ry's cross, Where He died to save you

So lov-ing and true, How can you re-fuse Him? O heed His sweet call,
Why lon-ger de-lay? O heart full of sor-row, There's comfort to-day,
Is wait-ing for you? Come now and re-ceive Him, To Sa-tan say nay,
At in-fi-nite cost; His heart there was bro-ken For you and for me,

CHORUS

O don't turn the Sav-ior a-way.... Don't turn the
Don't turn the Sav-ior a-

Sav-ior a-way, Don't turn the Sav-ior a-way; O hear Him
way from your heart, Don't turn the Sav-ior a-way from your heart;

rit.

plead-ing, O list to His call, O don't turn the Sav-ior a-way....

116 WHEN I THINK OF CALVARY

Rev. A. H. Ackley   B. D. Ackley

SOLO. *Tempo ad lib.*

1. I can hear the cry of a bro-ken heart, When I think of Cal - va - ry;
2. What He suffered there I shall al-ways see, When I think of Cal - va - ry;
3. So I call Him mine, this e-ter-nal Friend, When I think of Cal - va - ry;

Such a lov-ing grief makes the teardrops start, When I think of Cal - va - ry. . . .
What He did is more than all else to me, When I think of Cal - va - ry. . . .
And He waits for me at the journey's end, When I think of Cal - va - ry. . . .

REFRAIN

When I think of Cal - va - ry . . . . I think of His love for me, . . .

I vow to be true, And to love Jesus, too, When I think of Cal-va - ry. . . .

117 ROCKED IN THE CRADLE OF THE DEEP

Emma Willard

Joseph P. Knight

1. Rock'd in the cra-dle of the deep, I lay me down in peace to sleep;
2. And such the trust that still were mine, Tho' stormy winds sweep o'er the brine,

Se - cure I rest up - on the wave, For Thou, O Lord, hast pow'r to save.
Or though the tempest's fier-y breath Rouse me from sleep to wreck and death,

I know Thou wilt not slight my call, For Thou dost mark the sparrow's fall;
In o - cean cave still safe with Thee, The germ of im-mor-tal - i - ty;

And calm and peaceful is my sleep, Rocked in the cra-dle of the deep;

And calm and peaceful is my sleep, Rocked in the cra-dle of the deep.

118 MAKE A LITTLE RAINBOW OF YOUR TEARS

A. H. A.

Rev. A. H. Ackley

1. When its rain-ing and the sun is shin-ing, You can see a rain-bow
2. When your heart is overwhelmed with sad-ness, And the tears of grief are
3. When the fair-est dreams of life are brok-en, When its cherished friendships

in the sky, All its glo-ry is of love's de-sign-ing Sent to make you
fall-ing, too, Let His sunshine fill your heart with gladness, He will make a
pass a-way, When your heart is weighed with grief unspoken There's a rainbow

CHORUS

know that God is nigh. Make a lit-tle rainbow of your tears,......
rain-bow just for you.
for your darkest day.   of your tears,

It will help to drive a-way your fears,..... Let the Light Divine thro' the
                                      all your fears,

tears of sor-row shine, Make a lit-tle rainbow of your tears......
                                                          of your tears.

119 THE VALLEY OF PEACE

Mrs. Frank A. Breck

I. H. Meredith

With expression

1. There's a beau-ti-ful val-ley of peace, Where the heart of the wea-ry may rest;
2. In that beau-ti-ful val-ley I know Wild clam-or is hushed in-to calm;
3. In the val-ley of peace I may hide, Where strifes of the world cannot mar,
4. In the val-ley of peace let me roam With Je-sus, my "Staff" and my "Rod,"

Where tu-mult of tri-als may cease, And those who are burdened be blest.
And, walk-ing where still wa-ters flow, The sor-row-ing soul find-eth balm.
And there I will fol-low my Guide, My Hope and my glo-ri-ous Star;
Till I come to my heav-en-ly home, Whose builder and mak-er is God.

CHORUS

In the val-ley of peace, the val-ley of peace, In the

beau-ti-ful val-ley of peace, My Sav-ior is there ev-'ry

bur-den to bear, In the beau-ti-ful val-ley of peace. . . .
the val-ley of peace.

120 OH, IT IS WONDERFUL

COPYRIGHT, 1926, BY CHAS. H. GABRIEL. RENEWAL
HOMER A. RODEHEAVER, OWNER

C. H. G.

Chas. H. Gabriel

1. I stand all amazed at the love Je-sus of-fers me, Confused at the
2. I mar-vel that He would descend from His throne divine, To res-cue a
3. I think of his hands pierced and bleeding to pay the debt! Such mercy, such

grace that so ful-ly He proffers me; I tremble to know that for me He was
soul so re-bel-lious and proud as mine; That He should extend His great love unto
love and de-vo-tion can I forget? No, no! I will praise and a-dore at the

rit.

cru-ci-fied—That for me, a sin-ner, He suf-fered, He bled, and died.
such as I; Suf-fi-cient to own, to re-deem, and to jus-ti-fy.
mer-cy-seat, Un-til at the glo-ri-fied throne I kneel at His feet.

REFRAIN.

rit.

Oh, it is won-der-ful that He should care for me! E-nough to
won-der-ful!

die for me! Oh, it is won-der-ful, won-der-ful to me!
won-der-ful!

121 IF I COULD HEAR MY MOTHER PRAY AGAIN

James Rowe   J. W. VAUGHAN, OWNER.   BY PERMISSION   J. W. Vaughan

Slowly, with feeling

1. How sweet and hap-py seem those days of which I dream, When mem-o-ry re-
2. She used to pray that I on Je-sus would re - ly, And al-ways walk the
3. Her work on earth is done, the life-crown has been won, And she will be at

calls them now and then! And with that rapture sweet my weary heart would beat,
shin-ing gos - pel way: So trust-ing still His love, I seek that home a-bove,
rest with Him a - bove; And some glad morning she, I know, will welcome me

CHORUS

If I could hear my mother pray a - gain. If I could hear my
Where I shall meet my mother some glad day. If I could on-ly hear
To that e - ter-nal home of peace and love.

If I could only hear my

moth-er pray again, If I could hear her tender voice as then! So glad I'd
If I could only hear So happy I should

So hap - py

be, 'twould mean so much to me, If I could hear my mother pray a-gain.

I should be,

122 GOD'S WAY

Lida Shivers Leech

Lida Shivers Leech

DUET. *Espressivo*

1. God's way is the best way, Tho' I may not see Why sor-rows and
2. God's way is the best way, My path He hath planned, I'll trust in Him
3. God's way shall be my way, He know-eth the best, And lean-ing up-

tri - als Oft gath - er 'round me; He ev - er is seek - ing
al - way While hold-ing His hand. In shad-ow or sun-shine
on Him, Sweet, sweet is my rest. No harm can be - fall me,

My gold to re - fine, So hum-bly I trust Him, My Sav-ior di - vine.
He ev - er is near, With Him for my ref - uge, I nev-er need fear.
Safe, safe shall I be, I'll cling to Him ev - er, So pre-cious is He.

CHORUS *Animato*

God's way is the best way, God's way is the right way,

rit.

I'll trust in Him al - way, He know-eth the best.

123 GOD IS WORKING OUT HIS PURPOSE

Mrs. F. W. Suffield   COPYRIGHT, 1930, BY MRS. F. W. SUFFIELD   Mrs. F. W. Suffield

1. God is work-ing out His pur-pose He has planned for you and me:
2. God is work-ing out His pur-pose, E-ven tho' we go a-lone:
3. God is work-ing out His pur-pose, Tho' it lead thro' des-ert bare;
4. God is work-ing out His pur-pose, Nev-er mur-mur or re-pine;

Tho' from us it may be hid-den, Some day we will plain-ly see
It may take us from our loved ones, Lead us far a-way from home;
He'll go with us on life's jour-ney, And our heav-y bur-dens share;
For our fu-ture's in His keep-ing, Glad-ly to His will re-sign.

How He stands be-hind the shad-ows, Wait-ing to per-form His will,
It will be the great-est pleas-ure Just to feel His pres-ence near,
Thro' the wea-ry years of wait-ing, When the heart cries, "Lord, how long?"
When the veil at last is lift-ed, And the shad-ows flee a-way,

Whisp'ring, "Child, be of good cour-age, Ev-'ry prom-ise I'll ful-fill."
And to know that God is work-ing Out the pur-pose to Him dear.
God is work-ing out His pur-pose, Right will tri-umph o-ver wrong.
We shall un-der-stand His pur-pose Thro' one glad e-ter-nal day.

124 THE LAND WHERE THE ROSES NEVER FADE

E. E. Hewitt

B. D. Ackley

SOLO. *Moderato con espressione*

L. H.

1. When the cold breath of sorrow blights our joys,   Let us trust in our
2. When our hopes fall like leaves before the blast,   We should nev-er be
3. Work-ing on, trust-ing ev-er in His love,   Let our hearts on our

pp

L. H.

Fa-ther un-dis-mayed;   There is gladness no win-try grief de-stroys,
troubled, nor a-fraid,   For in Je - sus, we'll gather home at last,
Sav-ior still be stayed;   For we know we shall see His face a-bove,

CHORUS

In the Land where the roses nev-er fade.   In the Land where the roses nev-er

fade, ... Where no sin, neither sorrow dare in-vade,   We shall meet our loved ones

there, And e-ter-nal glories share, In the Land where the roses never fade.

125 JESUS CHRIST IS WONDERFUL

A. H. Ackley   A. H. Ackley

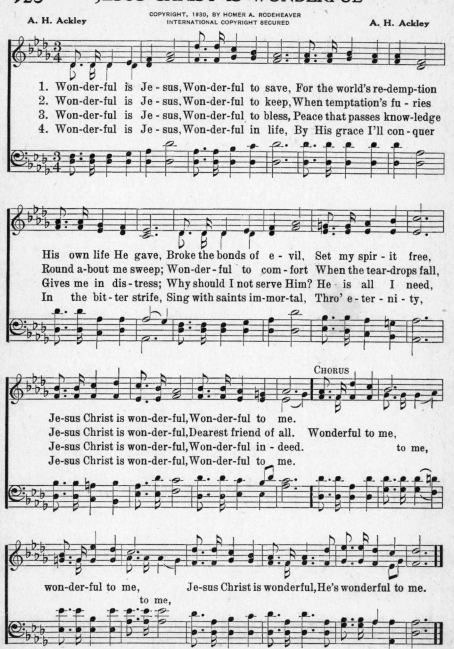

1. Won-der-ful is Je-sus, Won-der-ful to save, For the world's re-demp-tion
2. Won-der-ful is Je-sus, Won-der-ful to keep, When temptation's fu-ries
3. Won-der-ful is Je-sus, Won-der-ful to bless, Peace that passes know-ledge
4. Won-der-ful is Je-sus, Won-der-ful in life, By His grace I'll con-quer

His own life He gave, Broke the bonds of e-vil, Set my spir-it free,
Round a-bout me sweep; Won-der-ful to com-fort When the tear-drops fall,
Gives me in dis-tress; Why should I not serve Him? He is all I need,
In the bit-ter strife, Sing with saints im-mor-tal, Thro' e-ter-ni-ty,

CHORUS

Je-sus Christ is won-der-ful, Won-der-ful to me.
Je-sus Christ is won-der-ful, Dearest friend of all.   Wonderful to me,
Je-sus Christ is won-der-ful, Won-der-ful in-deed.   to me,
Je-sus Christ is won-der-ful, Won-der-ful to me.

won-der-ful to me,   Je-sus Christ is wonderful, He's wonderful to me.
        to me,

126 CARRY THY BURDEN TO JESUS

Ethel Verne King

Allegretto moderato.

Robert Hood Bowers

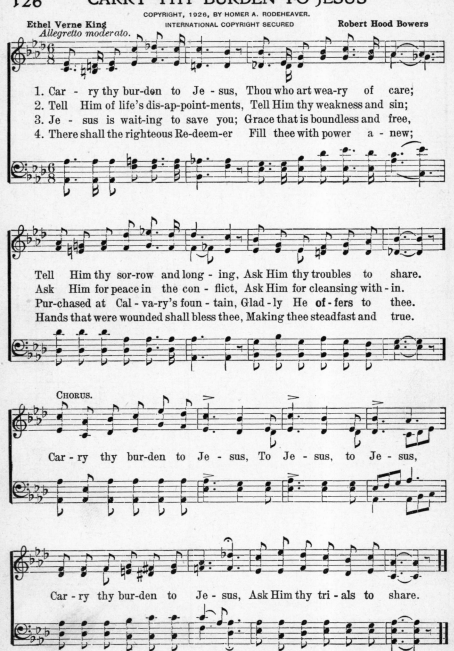

1. Car - ry thy bur-den to Je - sus, Thou who art wea-ry of care;
2. Tell Him of life's dis-ap-point-ments, Tell Him thy weakness and sin;
3. Je - sus is wait-ing to save you; Grace that is boundless and free,
4. There shall the righteous Re-deem-er Fill thee with power a - new;

Tell Him thy sor-row and long - ing, Ask Him thy troubles to share.
Ask Him for peace in the con - flict, Ask Him for cleansing with - in.
Pur-chased at Cal - va-ry's foun - tain, Glad - ly He of - fers to thee.
Hands that were wounded shall bless thee, Making thee steadfast and true.

CHORUS.

Car - ry thy bur-den to Je - sus, To Je - sus, to Je - sus,

Car - ry thy bur-den to Je - sus, Ask Him thy tri - als to share.

127 WHEN YOU KNOW JESUS, TOO

Ina Duley Ogdon

B. D. Ackley

1. When you my Je - sus un - der - stand, When you ac-
2. His joy will glad - den ev - 'ry day, His bless - ing
3. You'll see His mer - cy thro' your tears, His peace will
4. You'll know His way is al - ways best, And glad - ly

cept His lov - ing hand, A hap - py morn will dawn for you,
shine a - long the way, And you will share His prom - ise true,
hal - low all the years, The val - ley holds no dread for you,
leave to Him the rest, And tell what He has done for you,

CHORUS

When you know Je - sus, too. When you know Him, when you know Him,

You'll love Him just as oth - ers do; as oth - ers do; A

hap - py morn will dawn for you When you know my Je - sus, too.

128 NOT DREAMING

Gipsy Smith   **E. Edwin Young**

DUET

1. The world says I'm dreaming, but I know 'tis Je-sus Who saves me from
2. My home in the glo-ry is fair-er than morn-ing, And Je-sus my
3. Oh, let me fight on for Je-sus my Sav-ior, And tell of the

bond-age and sin's guilt-y stain; He is my Lov-er, my
Sav-ior will wel-come me there; No, I'm not dream-ing! I'm a-
love He so won-drous-ly gave; Preaching or sing-ing, or

Sav-ior, my Mas-ter, 'Tis He who has freed me from guilt and its pain.
wake, it is dawn-ing, His smile and His love I'll e-ter-nal-ly share.
liv-ing or dy-ing, In life or in death He is might-y to save.

CHORUS

Let me dream on,   If I am dreaming; Let me dream on,   My sins are gone;
Let me dream on, dream on;   My sins are gone;

Night turns to dawn, Love's light is beaming, So if I'm dreaming, Let me dream on.
Night turns to dawn's bright beam-ing,   Let me dream on, dream on.

129 YOU CAN SMILE

A. H. A.

A. H. Ackley

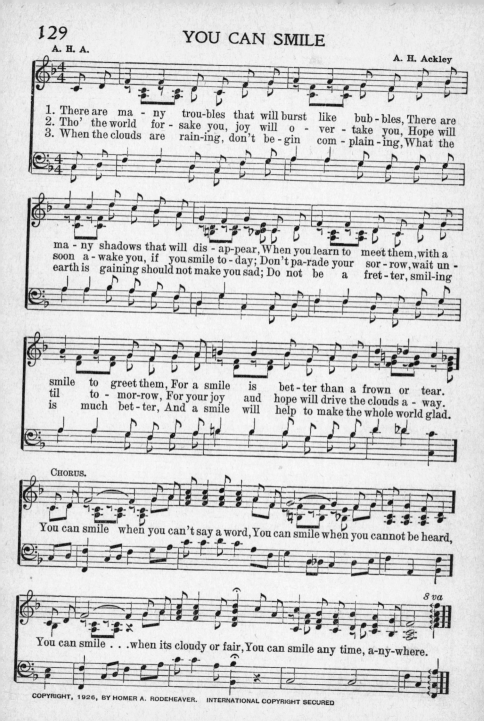

1. There are ma - ny trou-bles that will burst like bub - bles, There are
2. Tho' the world for - sake you, joy will o - ver - take you, Hope will
3. When the clouds are rain-ing, don't be - gin com - plain-ing, What the

ma - ny shadows that will dis - ap-pear, When you learn to meet them, with a
soon a - wake you, if you smile to - day; Don't pa-rade your sor - row, wait un -
earth is gaining should not make you sad; Do not be a fret - ter, smil-ing

smile to greet them, For a smile is bet - ter than a frown or tear.
til to - mor-row, For your joy aud hope will drive the clouds a - way.
is much bet - ter, And a smile will help to make the whole world glad.

CHORUS.

You can smile when you can't say a word, You can smile when you cannot be heard,

8 va

You can smile . . . when its cloudy or fair, You can smile any time, a-ny-where.

SOMEONE'S LAST CALL

Edna R. Worrwell   Clarence B. Strouse. Arr.

1. Come, O come to the bless-ed Sav - ior, List, O list to His
2. Deep, deep, deep in the heart there whis - pers God's own voice to each
3. Long, long, long have you tried to sti - fle Yearnings sweet to a
4. Now, *now*, NOW as the Spir-it stirs . . . you, Hard-en not your fast

lov - ing call, Of - fer - ing par - don, Par-don from sin to
way-ward child; Heed it! O heed it! Be no more sin - be-
life more pure; Quench them no lon - ger But in God rest se-
melt-ing heart; Take, take sal - va - tion Else shall your chance de-

all; O come, He gives par-don from sin to all, to all.
guiled, O heed His voice, be now no more be-guiled, be - guiled.
cure; O strive no more, but in God rest se - cure, se - cure.
part; O take it *now*, else shall your chance depart, de - part.

REFRAIN

Come, come to Je - sus, Come ere this mo-ment takes flight;

It may be now some-one's last call, last call to - night.

131 ON WINGS OF PRAYER

Korean Folk Song

English Words by
Anne Campbell

Transcribed and Arr. by
Rody C. Hyun

Andante

1. When the white ship sails o-ver the bil-lows Near to the land of sin and
2. O - ver the sea the morning sun ris - es; Out of the tem-pest peace will

woe, Je - sus will bring me safe to the har - bor; I will not
come. Prayer is the light that con-quers my dark-ness, Prayer is the

fear the storms that blow. Help me to sail on wings of Thy
hand that leads me Home. When I am pray - ing, God's voice is

Spir - it; Give me the strength my bur-dens to bear. Ah! Thy love hath
call - ing, I am re - leased from sor - row and care. Ah! His love hath

pow'r to car-ry me on - ward, Sail-ing to Je - sus on wings of prayer.
pow'r to car-ry me on - ward, Sail-ing to Je - sus on wings of prayer.

132

EARTH IS THE GIFT OF GOD

From the Korean

English Words by
Anne Campbell

Transcribed and Arr. by
Rody C. Hyun

1. Soft winds are mur - mur-ing, Mead-ows are blos - som-ing;
2. Moon-beams are shim - mer-ing, Home lights are glim - mer-ing;

O - ver the field comes the shep - - herd,
Now comes the end of the jour - - ney.

Toil - ing and car - ol-ing, Joy in the har - vest-ing,
Praise God who gave to us Our world so glo - ri-ous,

Earth is the glo - ri - ous gift of God.
Earth is the glo - ri - ous gift of God.

133 THE EASTERN GATE

Dedicated to Rev. P. F. Bresee, Los Angeles, Cal.

I. G. Martin

Arr. I. G. Martin

1. I will meet you in the morn-ing, Just in-side the East-ern Gate;
2. If you has-ten off to glo-ry, Lin-ger near the East-ern Gate,
3. Keep your lamps all trimmed and burning, For the Bridegroom watch and wait;
4. O, the joy of that glad meet-ing With the saints who for us wait!

Then be read-y, faith-ful pil-grim, Lest with you it be too late.
For I'm com-ing in the morn-ing, So you'll not have long to wait.
He'll be with us at the meet-ing, Just in-side the East-ern Gate.
What a bless-ed hap-py meet-ing, Just in-side the East-ern Gate!

CHORUS

I will meet you, in the morn-ing, I will meet you, in the morn-ing, Just in-side the East-ern Gate o-ver there; I will meet you, in the morn-ing, I will meet you, in the morn-ing, I will meet you in the morn-ing o-ver there.

134 HOW COULD I LIVE WITHOUT JESUS?

George W. Cooke

George W. Cooke

DUET. *Sop. and Alto*

1. How could I live with-out Je - sus, my All? He will sup-
2. How could I walk with-out Je - sus, my Friend, Life's drear - y
3. How could I hope with-out Je - sus, my Guide? He is my
4. How could I die with-out Je - sus, my Light— Go through death's

port me, what-e'er may be - fall; "Come un - to Me, wea - ry
path - way, thorn-strewn to the end? "Fear not, I'm with thee, thy
Day - star, com - pan - ion be - side, Lead - ing me safe - ly, what-
val - ley to man - sions so bright? Christ my Re-deem - er will

one," He doth call, Je - - sus, bless - ed Je - - sus.
soul to de - fend:" Je - - sus, lov - ing Je - - sus.
e'er may be - tide, Je - - sus, pre-cious Je - - sus.
ban - ish the night: Je - - sus, on - ly Je - - sus.

CHORUS

1-3. How could I live? How could I live? How could I live with-out Je - sus?
4. How could I die? How could I die? *etc.*

Sav - ior di - vine— I know He is mine: How could I live with-out Je - sus?

135 THE LAST MILE OF THE WAY

Rev. Johnson Oatman
Wm. Edie Marks

1. If I walk in the path-way of du - ty, If I work till the
2. If for Christ I pro-claim the glad sto - ry, If I seek for His
3. Here the dear-est of ties we must sev - er, Tears of sor - row are
4. And if here I have ear-nest-ly striv-en, And have tried all His

close of the day; I shall see the great King in His beau-ty, When I've
sheep gone a - stray, I am sure He will show me His glo - ry, When I've
seen ev - 'ry day; But no sick-ness, no sigh-ing for - ev - er, When I've
will to o - bey, 'Twill en-hance all the rap-ture of heav - en, When I've

CHORUS

gone the last mile of the way. When I've gone the last mile of the

way, ... I will rest at the close of the day, . . . And I
of the way, of the day,

know there are joys that a - wait me; When I've gone the last mile of the way.

THE OLD-FASHIONED MEETING

H. B.

Herbert Buffum

1. Oh, how well I re - mem-ber in the old-fash - ioned days, When some
2. There was singing, such sing-ing, of those old-fash - ioned airs! There was
3. Well, they say it is better, "Things have changed, don't you know," And the
4. If the Lord nev - er chang-es, as the fashions of men, If He's

old - fash - ioned peo - ple had some old - fash - ioned ways; In the
pow - er, such pow - er in those old - fash - ioned pray'rs, An old -
peo - ple in gen - 'ral, seem to think it is so; And they
al - ways the same, why, He is old - fash - ioned, then! As an

old - fash-ioned meet-ings, as they tar - ried there, In the old - fash-ioned
fashioned con - vic - tion made the sin - ner pray, And the Lord heard and
call me old - fash-ioned when I dare to say, That I like it far
old - fash-ioned sin - ner saved thro' old-time grace, Oh, I'm sure He will

CHORUS.

man - ner, how God an-swered their pray'r.
saved Him, in the old - fash-ioned way. 'Twas an old-fash-ioned meeting,
bet - ter in the old - fash - ioned way.
take me to an old - fash - ioned place.

in an old-fash-ioned place, Where some old - fash-ioned peo - ple had some

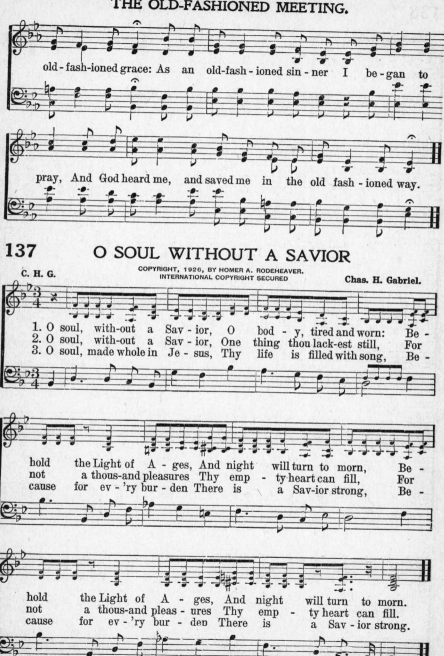

old-fash-ioned grace: As an old-fash-ioned sin-ner I be-gan to

pray, And God heard me, and saved me in the old fash-ioned way.

137   O SOUL WITHOUT A SAVIOR

C. H. G.

Chas. H. Gabriel.

1. O soul, with-out a Sav-ior, O bod-y, tired and worn: Be-
2. O soul, with-out a Sav-ior, One thing thou lack-est still, For
3. O soul, made whole in Je-sus, Thy life is filled with song, Be-

hold the Light of A-ges, And night will turn to morn, Be-
not a thous-and pleasures Thy emp-ty heart can fill, For
cause for ev-'ry bur-den There is a Sav-ior strong, Be-

hold the Light of A-ges, And night will turn to morn.
not a thous-and pleas-ures Thy emp-ty heart can fill.
cause for ev-'ry bur-den There is a Sav-ior strong.

138 JESUS

Ina Duley Ogden
Not too fast.

B. D. Ackley

1. There is a name I love to hear, Je - sus, bless - ed Je - sus!
2. There is a pic - ture in my heart, Je - sus, bless - ed Je - sus!
3. There is a sa - cred mem - o - ry, Je - sus, bless - ed Je - sus!
4. There is a home in love di - vine, Je - sus, bless - ed Je - sus!

It falls like mu - sic on my ear, Je - sus, bless - ed Je - sus!
It makes the lov - ing tear-drops start, Je - sus, bless - ed Je - sus!
Of Beth - le - hem to Cal - va - ry, Je - sus, bless - ed Je - sus!
I am so glad that He is mine, Je - sus, bless - ed Je - sus!

CHORUS.

No oth - er is so dear to me, As Je - sus, Lamb of Cal - va - ry,

His precious life He gave for me, Je - sus, bless-ed Je - sus!

139 THROUGH LOVE TO LIGHT

Rev. A. N. Ackley

B. D. Ackley

DUET. *Soprano and Tenor*

1. Through love to light Thou lead-est me; The light that fills my way
2. Through love to faith Thou lead-est me; I know the God I own;
3. Through love to life Thou lead-est me; Tho' dead, to pu - ri - ty,

Il - lu-mines all the val-leys deep, And drives my fear a - way.
He binds me to His bro-ken heart, And makes my cause His own.
Thy mer - cy broke the tomb of sin And set my spir - it free.

CHORUS

Through love to peace Thou lead-est me; And oh, such peace is mine,

Sur-pass-ing ev - 'ry earth-ly joy, The peace of love di - vine.

140 THE SHEPHERD OF LOVE

Albert Simpson Reitz   Albert Simpson Reitz

DUET.

1. The Shep-herd of Love is seek-ing the lost In paths that are
2. The Shep-herd of Love knows His sheep by name, And ten-der-ly
3. The Shep-herd of Love our ran-som hath paid, And of-fers sal-
4. The Shep-herd of Love now seek-eth His sheep, He seek-eth what-

rough and steep; He's call-ing the lambs that have gone a-stray,
leads the way; O wea-ry one, come to the Shepherd's fold,
va-tion free; He's pa-tient-ly wait-ing for thee to come,
e'er the cost; Be-hold, He is call-ing the wan-d'rer home,

rit.   CHORUS.

He's call-ing, call-ing His sheep.
He's call-ing, call-ing to-day.
He's call-ing, call-ing for thee.   Call-ing,
He's call-ing, call-ing the lost.

Out of your dark-ness of

sin and shame, In-to His love, for-ev-er the same; Come to Him
call-ing, Call-ing, call-ing,

ad lib.

now, be-lieve on His name, O an-swer the call to-day.

141 ONLY SHADOWS.

A. H. A.   A. H. Ackley.

1. There are shadows of sorrow that darken life's way, They are on-ly
2. There are shadows of fear bringing tho'ts that dis-may, They are on-ly
3. There are shadows of doubt that steal in-to our mind, They are on-ly
4. There are shadows of death that are black with despair, They are on-ly

shad-ows, But be-hind the dark shadows shines love's kind-ly ray,
shad-ows, If we walk in His love they will all pass a-way,
shad-ows, If we look to the cross blest as-sur-ance we find,
shad-ows, For Christ Je-sus, the Light of the world, will be there,

CHORUS.

They are on-ly shad-ows. Do not doubt, do not fear, When the

shadows ap-pear, Just re-mem-ber that dark lone-ly shad-ows Can-not

hide God's dear face, If we trust in His grace, They are on-ly shad-ows.

142 WHAT WILL YOU DO WITH THE SAVIOR?

"What shall I do then with Jesus, which is called Christ"—MATT. 27: 22

Cabell Foster Smith   Cabell Foster Smith

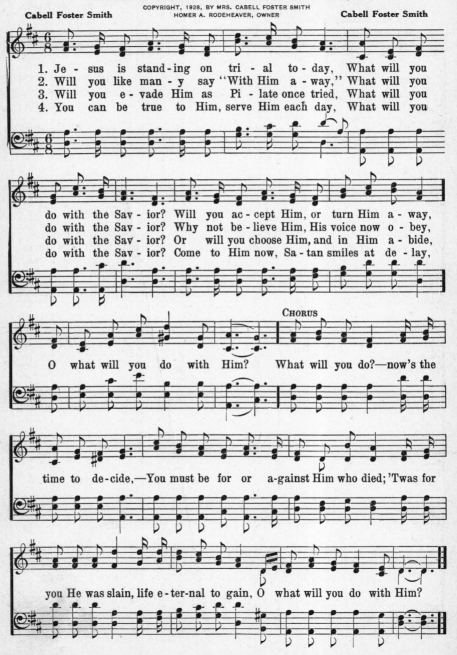

1. Je - sus is stand-ing on tri - al to - day, What will you
2. Will you like man - y say "With Him a - way," What will you
3. Will you e - vade Him as Pi - late once tried, What will you
4. You can be true to Him, serve Him each day, What will you

do with the Sav - ior? Will you ac - cept Him, or turn Him a - way,
do with the Sav - ior? Why not be - lieve Him, His voice now o - bey,
do with the Sav - ior? Or will you choose Him, and in Him a - bide,
do with the Sav - ior? Come to Him now, Sa - tan smiles at de - lay,

CHORUS

O what will you do with Him? What will you do?—now's the

time to de-cide,—You must be for or a-gainst Him who died; 'Twas for

you He was slain, life e - ter-nal to gain, O what will you do with Him?

143 I'LL SERVE HIM TO-DAY

C. Benj. Hopkins

Chas. H. Marsh

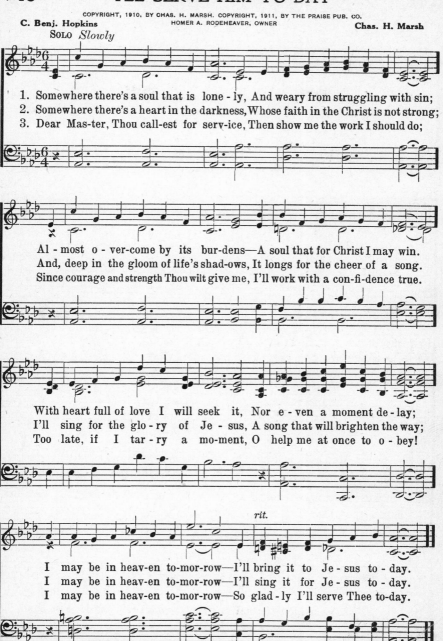

1. Somewhere there's a soul that is lone-ly, And weary from struggling with sin;
2. Somewhere there's a heart in the darkness, Whose faith in the Christ is not strong;
3. Dear Mas-ter, Thou call-est for serv-ice, Then show me the work I should do;

Al-most o-ver-come by its bur-dens—A soul that for Christ I may win.
And, deep in the gloom of life's shad-ows, It longs for the cheer of a song.
Since courage and strength Thou wilt give me, I'll work with a con-fi-dence true.

With heart full of love I will seek it, Nor e-ven a moment de-lay;
I'll sing for the glo-ry of Je-sus, A song that will brighten the way;
Too late, if I tar-ry a mo-ment, O help me at once to o-bey!

I may be in heav-en to-mor-row—I'll bring it to Je-sus to-day.
I may be in heav-en to-mor-row—I'll sing it for Je-sus to-day.
I may be in heav-en to-mor-row—So glad-ly I'll serve Thee to-day.

144 BE STILL AND KNOW

Mrs. Hal Buckner
DUET.

B. B. McKinney

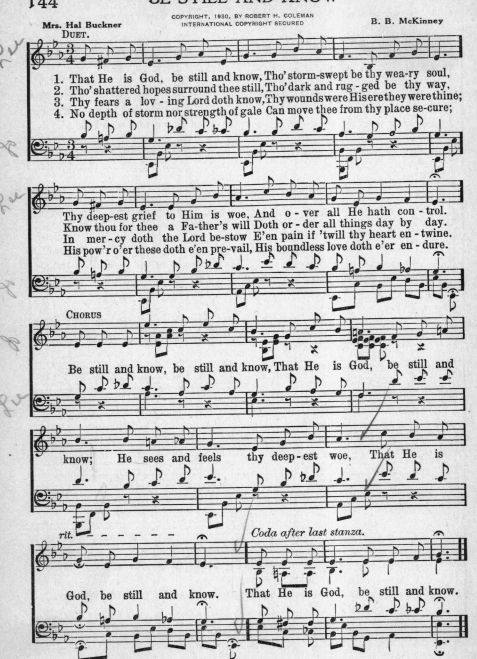

1. That He is God, be still and know, Tho' storm-swept be thy wea-ry soul,
2. Tho' shattered hopes surround thee still, Tho' dark and rug-ged be thy way,
3. Thy fears a lov-ing Lord doth know, Thy wounds were His ere they were thine;
4. No depth of storm nor strength of gale Can move thee from thy place se-cure;

Thy deep-est grief to Him is woe, And o-ver all He hath con-trol.
Know thou for thee a Fa-ther's will Doth or-der all things day by day.
In mer-cy doth the Lord be-stow E'en pain if 'twill thy heart en-twine.
His pow'r o'er these doth e'en pre-vail, His boundless love doth e'er en-dure.

CHORUS

Be still and know, be still and know, That He is God, be still and know; He sees and feels thy deep-est woe, That He is

rit. Coda after last stanza.

God, be still and know. That He is God, be still and know.

145 WHERE WE'LL NEVER GROW OLD

Dedicated to my Father and Mother

JAS. C. MOORE, OWNER

Jas. C. Moore

Jas. C. Moore

Effectively

1. I have heard of a land on the far - a - way strand, 'Tis a
2. In that beau - ti - ful home where we'll nev - er - more roam, We shall
3. When our work here is done and the life - crown is won, And our

beau - ti - ful home of the soul; Built by Je - sus on high, there we
be in the sweet by and by; Hap - py praise to the King thro' e -
troub - les and tri - als are o'er, All our sor - row will end, and our

nev - er shall die, 'Tis a land where we nev - er grow old.
ter - ni - ty sing, 'Tis a land where we nev - er shall die.
voic - es will blend With the loved ones who've gone on be - fore.

CHORUS

Nev-er grow old, nev-er grow old, In a land where we'll never grow old;

Where we'll

Nev-er grow old, nev-er grow old, In a land where we'll never grow old.

Where we'll

146 WHEN I GET TO THE END OF THE WAY

Charlie D. Tillman

1. The sands have been washed in the foot-prints Of the Stran-ger on
2. He loves me too well to for-sake me Or give me one
3. There are so man-y hills to climb up-ward I oft-en am
4. When the last fee-ble steps have been tak-en And the gates of that

D. C.— And the toils of the road will seem noth-ing, When I get to the
Last v.—Then the toils of the road will seem noth-ing, When I get to the

Gal - i - lee's shore, And the voice that sub-dued the rough bil - lows
tri - al too much; All His peo - ple have been dear-ly pur-chased,
long-ing for rest, But He who ap-points me my path-way
cit - y ap - pear, And the beau - ti - ful songs of the an - gels

end of the way; And the toils of the road will seem noth - ing,
end of the way; Then the toils of the road will seem noth - ing,

FINE.

Will be heard in Ju - de - a no more. But the path of that
And Sa - tan can nev - er claim such. By and by I shall
Knows just what is need - ful and best. I know in His
Float out on my lis - ten - ing ear; When all that now

When I get to the end of the way.
When I get to the end of the way.

D. C.

lone Gal - i - le - an With joy I will fol - low to - day;
see Him and praise Him, In the cit - y of un - end - ing day;
word He hath prom - ised That my strength, "it shall be as my day;"
seems so mys - te - rious Will be bright and as clear as the day,

147 WELL DONE

J. W. Van DeVenter

J. W. Van DeVenter

DUET

1. When night-shades are fall-ing And work is no more, I rest at the
2. My day is fast wan-ing, The sun-set is near, A few fleet-ing
3. Ere la-bors are end-ed, My life is com-plete, May I be of

close of life's day, When care-worn and wea-ry I wait to pass
mo-ments to stay, May these be the sweet-est Of all I hold
serv-ice, I pray, And win pre-cious jew-els To lay at His

CHORUS

o'er, At last, may I hear Je-sus say:
dear, And then, may I hear Je-sus say: "Well done, be-lov-ed, Your
feet, And then, may I hear Je-sus say:

work is well done, The cross, that I gave you, lay down; Your task is

o-ver, The prize you have won, My child, I will give you a crown."

148 THE SAVIOR FOR ME

William M. Runyan   William M. Runyan

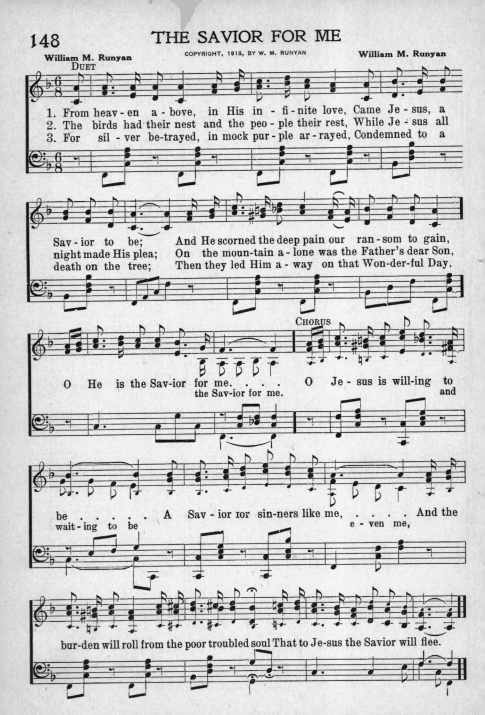

1. From heav-en a-bove, in His in-fi-nite love, Came Je-sus, a
2. The birds had their nest and the peo-ple their rest, While Je-sus all
3. For sil-ver be-trayed, in mock pur-ple ar-rayed, Condemned to a

Sav-ior to be;   And He scorned the deep pain our ran-som to gain,
night made His plea;   On the moun-tain a-lone was the Father's dear Son,
death on the tree;   Then they led Him a-way on that Won-der-ful Day,

CHORUS

O He is the Sav-ior for me. . . .   O Je-sus is will-ing to
the Sav-ior for me.   and

be . . . . A Sav-ior for sin-ners like me, ... And the
wait-ing to be   e-ven me,

bur-den will roll from the poor troubled soul That to Je-sus the Savior will flee.

149   TAKE THOU MY HAND

Mrs. Frank A. Breck

Chas. H. Marsh

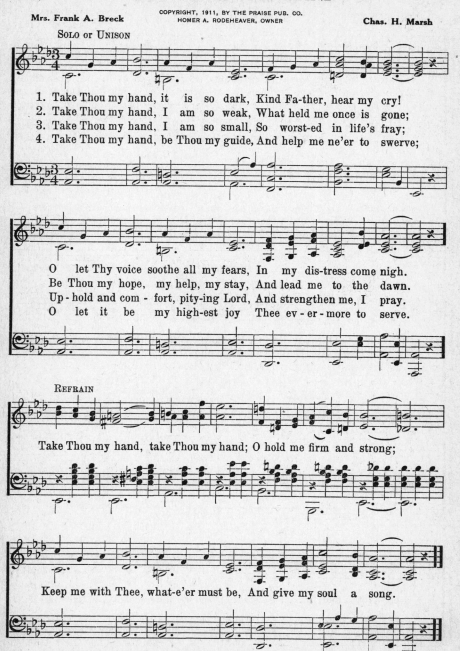

SOLO or UNISON

1. Take Thou my hand, it is so dark, Kind Fa-ther, hear my cry!
2. Take Thou my hand, I am so weak, What held me once is gone;
3. Take Thou my hand, I am so small, So worst-ed in life's fray;
4. Take Thou my hand, be Thou my guide, And help me ne'er to swerve;

O let Thy voice soothe all my fears, In my dis-tress come nigh.
Be Thou my hope, my help, my stay, And lead me to the dawn.
Up - hold and com - fort, pity-ing Lord, And strengthen me, I pray.
O let it be my high-est joy Thee ev - er - more to serve.

REFRAIN

Take Thou my hand, take Thou my hand; O hold me firm and strong;

Keep me with Thee, what-e'er must be, And give my soul a song.

150 WE WILL TALK IT O'ER TOGETHER

COPYRIGHT, 1915, BY E. O. EXCELL
WORDS AND MUSIC

Mrs. C. H. Morris   Mrs. C. H. Morris

1. We are trav'ling home to Heaven by the straight and narrow way, Which the
2. There with Mo-ses and E - li - as, and with Pe - ter and with Paul, We'll re-
3. We will look back o'er the journey by our heav'nly Father planned, Knowing

saints and mar-tyrs have be-fore us trod; In the cross of Christ we glo - ry
count the tri-umphs of re-deem-ing grace; Best of all, we'll see our Sav-ior,
that His will was best for you and me; And the things which here perplex us,

as we jour - ney day by day, Pressing onward to the cit - y of our God.
hail and crown Him Lord of all, And unite His praise to sing thro' endless days.
which we can - not un-der-stand, In that glorious day of days made plain will be.

D. S.—*reached our heav'nly home; We will talk it o'er to-geth-er by and by.*

CHORUS.

We will talk it o'er to-geth-er by and by, ... When we reach that holy
by and by,

cit - y, you and I, . . . How thro' grace we've overcome, and have A - MEN.

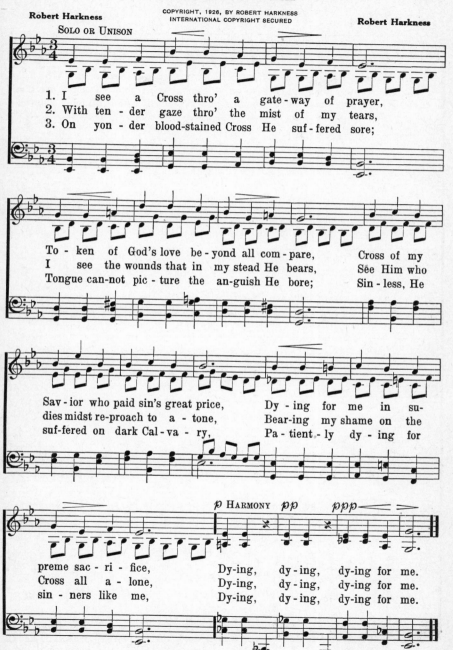

151 DYING FOR ME

Robert Harkness   Robert Harkness

SOLO OR UNISON

1. I see a Cross thro' a gate-way of prayer,
2. With ten-der gaze thro' the mist of my tears,
3. On yon-der blood-stained Cross He suf-fered sore;

To-ken of God's love be-yond all com-pare,   Cross of my
I see the wounds that in my stead He bears,   See Him who
Tongue can-not pic-ture the an-guish He bore;   Sin-less, He

Sav-ior who paid sin's great price,   Dy-ing for me in su-
dies midst re-proach to a-tone,   Bear-ing my shame on the
suf-fered on dark Cal-va-ry,   Pa-tient-ly dy-ing for

p HARMONY *pp*   *ppp*

preme sac-ri-fice,   Dy-ing, dy-ing, dy-ing for me.
Cross all a-lone,   Dy-ing, dy-ing, dy-ing for me.
sin-ners like me,   Dy-ing, dy-ing, dy-ing for me.

152 KEEP HOLDING ON TO GOD

Mrs. C. H. Morris   Mrs. C. H. Morris

1. Be not dis-mayed, keep pray-ing on, Night soon will
2. Are those you love the best to - day Still on the
3. Trust tho' the way you can-not see, Still fol-low
4. Keep pray-ing on what-e'er your need, He is the

fade, the morn - ing dawn; The fight of faith will
moun - tains bleak a - stray? Far from the fold of
on con-fid - ing - ly, The prayer of faith will
sin - ner's friend in - deed; His prom-is - es of

soon be won, Keep hold - ing on to God. . . . .
grace a - way? Keep hold - ing on to God. . . . .
an - swered be, Keep hold - ing on to God. . . . .
mer - cy plead, Keep hold - ing on to God. . . . .

CHORUS

Keep hold-ing on to God, Keep hold-ing on to God, Although the an-swer
Keep hold - ing on to God, Keep hold-ing on to God,

KEEP HOLDING ON TO GOD

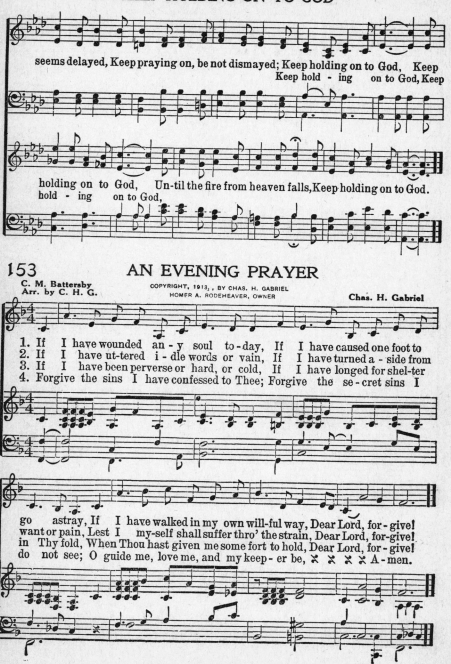

seems delayed, Keep praying on, be not dismayed; Keep holding on to God, Keep
Keep hold - ing on to God, Keep

holding on to God, Un-til the fire from heaven falls, Keep holding on to God.
hold - ing on to God,

AN EVENING PRAYER

153

C. M. Battersby
Arr. by C. H. G.

Chas. H. Gabriel

1. If I have wounded an-y soul to-day, If I have caused one foot to
2. If I have ut-tered i-dle words or vain, If I have turned a-side from
3. If I have been perverse or hard, or cold, If I have longed for shel-ter
4. Forgive the sins I have confessed to Thee; Forgive the se-cret sins I

go astray, If I have walked in my own will-ful way, Dear Lord, for-give!
want or pain, Lest I my-self shall suffer thro' the strain, Dear Lord, for-give!
in Thy fold, When Thou hast given me some fort to hold, Dear Lord, for-give!
do not see; O guide me, love me, and my keep-er be, A-men.

154 TELL MOTHER I'LL BE THERE

C. M. F.

CHARLES M. FILLMORE

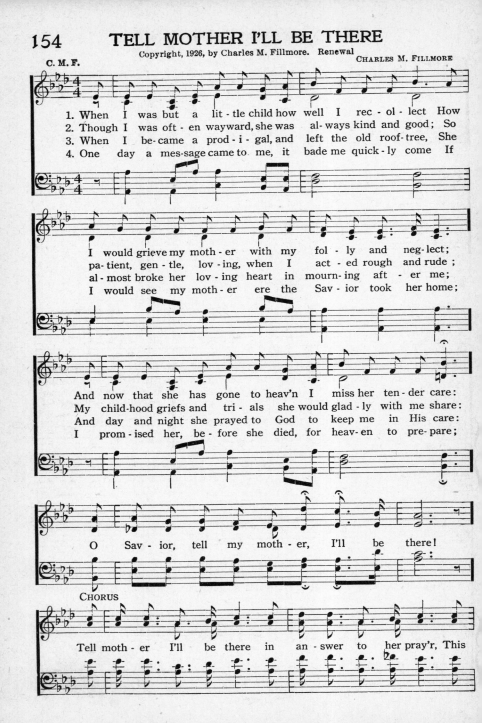

1. When I was but a lit-tle child how well I rec-ol-lect How
2. Though I was oft-en wayward, she was al-ways kind and good; So
3. When I be-came a prod-i-gal, and left the old roof-tree, She
4. One day a mes-sage came to me, it bade me quick-ly come If

I would grieve my moth-er with my fol-ly and neg-lect;
pa-tient, gen-tle, lov-ing, when I act-ed rough and rude;
al-most broke her lov-ing heart in mourn-ing aft-er me;
I would see my moth-er ere the Sav-ior took her home;

And now that she has gone to heav'n I miss her ten-der care:
My child-hood griefs and tri-als she would glad-ly with me share:
And day and night she prayed to God to keep me in His care:
I prom-ised her, be-fore she died, for heav-en to pre-pare;

O Sav-ior, tell my moth-er, I'll be there!

CHORUS

Tell moth-er I'll be there in an-swer to her pray'r, This

TELL MOTHER I'LL BE THERE

mes-sage, bless-ed Sav-ior, to her bear! Tell moth-er I'll be there, heav'n's

joys with her to share, Yes, tell my dar-ling moth-er I'll be there.

155 SOMETIME!

155

Robert Harkness   Robert Harkness

DUET

1. Some-time all sor-rows shall be o'er, Some-time! All earth-ly care be known no
2. Some-time our loved ones we shall greet, Some-time! When in the Father's house we
3. Some-time when sets at last life's sun, Some-time! Our jour-ney end-ed, la - bor
4. Some-time, I know not when 'twill be, Some-time! My Lord will come a-gain for

more! O what re-joic - ing on the golden shore,
meet, On - ly to sit for - ev - er at His feet, Some-time, some-time soon!
done, O what a crown for ev-'ry vict'ry won,   some-time soon!
me,   Then I shall reign with Him e-ter-nal-ly,

156 MY MOTHER

Rev. A. H. ACKLEY

B. D. ACKLEY

1. To my mem-'ry comes a vis-ion That my heart can ne'er for-get, Of my
2. 'Twas the voice of my dear moth-er, Full of love and sym-pa-thy, That so
3. Tho' my moth-er has de-part-ed, Still I feel her spir-it near, As she

moth-er, with her tender care for me,......... For the face of years for-got-ten
oft-en cheered my heart when sad and lone,...... For I felt the need of Je-sus,
pleads be-fore the Heav'nly Father's throne;... And her pray'rs my life shall answer,

Still remains, I see it yet, And her brow reflects the light of Calvary.
And her constant pray'r for me Led my wand'ring footsteps to my Father's home.
For I long to meet her there, And to see the Christ who bought me for His own.

CHORUS

And the tear-drops, how they glistened, When she told me of His love,

How the ten-der Shep-herd came to seek the lost,
Shep-herd came to seek and save the lost,

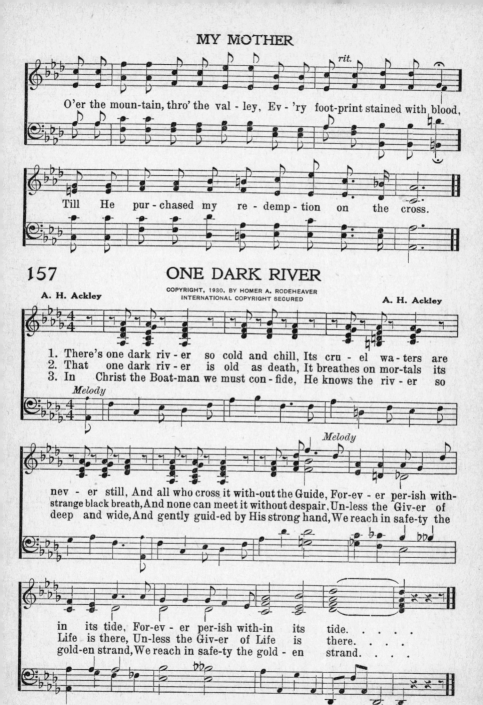

MY MOTHER

O'er the moun-tain, thro' the val - ley, Ev - 'ry foot-print stained with blood,

Till He pur-chased my re - demp - tion on the cross.

157   ## ONE DARK RIVER

A. H. Ackley   A. H. Ackley

1. There's one dark riv - er so cold and chill, Its cru - el wa - ters are
2. That one dark riv - er is old as death, It breathes on mor-tals its
3. In Christ the Boat-man we must con - fide, He knows the riv - er so

Melody

nev - er still, And all who cross it with-out the Guide, For-ev - er per-ish with-
strange black breath, And none can meet it without despair. Un-less the Giv-er of
deep and wide, And gently guid-ed by His strong hand, We reach in safe-ty the

Melody

in its tide, For-ev - er per-ish with-in its tide. . . . .
Life is there, Un-less the Giv-er of Life is there. . . . .
gold-en strand, We reach in safe-ty the gold - en strand. . . . .

WHY I LOVE HIM

158

E. E. Hewitt

B. D. Ackley

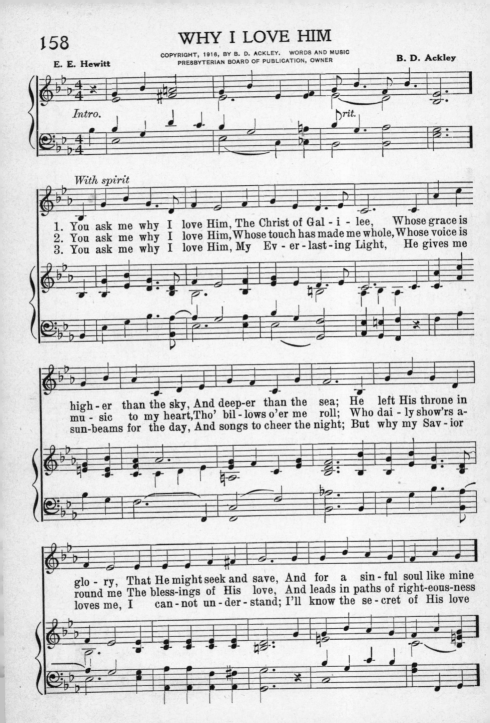

1. You ask me why I love Him, The Christ of Gal - i - lee, Whose grace is
2. You ask me why I love Him, Whose touch has made me whole, Whose voice is
3. You ask me why I love Him, My Ev - er - last - ing Light, He gives me

high - er than the sky, And deep-er than the sea; He left His throne in
mu - sic to my heart, Tho' bil - lows o'er me roll; Who dai - ly show'rs a-
sun-beams for the day, And songs to cheer the night; But why my Sav - ior

glo - ry, That He might seek and save, And for a sin - ful soul like mine
round me The bless-ings of His love, And leads in paths of right-eous-ness
loves me, I can - not un - der - stand; I'll know the se - cret of His love

His pre - cious blood He gave.
To man-sions built a - bove. You ask me why I love Him, And why He
In yon - der ra - diant land.

loves me so; Re-turn with me to Cal - va - ry, The rea-son then you'll know.

This Gospel Solo may be had on Edison Blue Amberol Record No. 3226.   All dealers

159   WHEN I CAN READ MY TITLE CLEAR

Isaac Watts

J. C. Lowry

1. When I can read my ti - tle clear, To man-sions in the skies, ...
2. Should earth a-gainst my soul en-gage, And fi - ery darts be hurled, ...
3. Let cares like a wild del - uge come, And storms of sor-row fall, ...
4. There I can bathe my wea - ry soul In seas of heav'n-ly rest, ...

I'll bid fare - well to ev - 'ry fear, And wipe my weep-ing eyes.
Then I can smile at Sa - tan's rage, And face a frown-ing world.
I know I'll safe - ly reach my home, My God, my heav'n, my all.
And not a wave of troub - le roll A - cross my peace-ful breast.

160 I HEARD THE VOICE OF JESUS SAY

Horatius Bonar

Old English Air

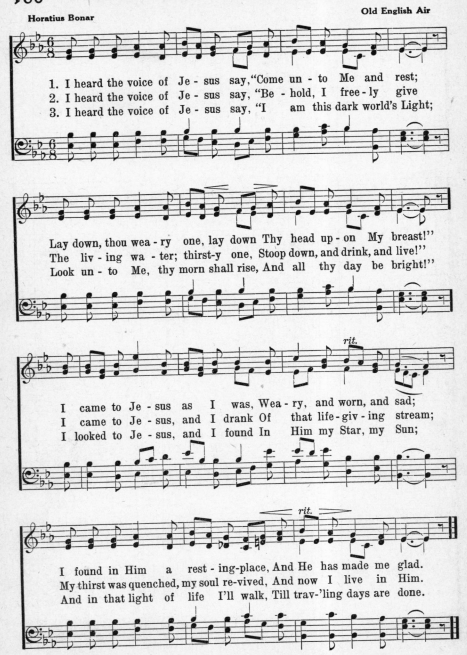

1. I heard the voice of Je-sus say, "Come un-to Me and rest;
2. I heard the voice of Je-sus say, "Be-hold, I free-ly give
3. I heard the voice of Je-sus say, "I am this dark world's Light;

Lay down, thou wea-ry one, lay down Thy head up-on My breast!"
The liv-ing wa-ter; thirst-y one, Stoop down, and drink, and live!"
Look un-to Me, thy morn shall rise, And all thy day be bright!"

I came to Je-sus as I was, Wea-ry, and worn, and sad;
I came to Je-sus, and I drank Of that life-giv-ing stream;
I looked to Je-sus, and I found In Him my Star, my Sun;

I found in Him a rest-ing-place, And He has made me glad.
My thirst was quenched, my soul re-vived, And now I live in Him.
And in that light of life I'll walk, Till trav-'ling days are done.

161 UNDER THE CROSS

Rev. A. H. Ackley

B. D. Ackley

DUET. *Tenor (or Soprano) and Alto*

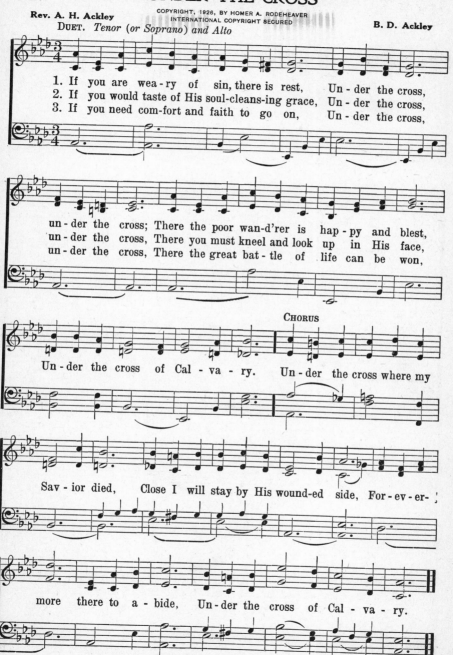

1. If you are wea-ry of sin, there is rest, Un-der the cross,
2. If you would taste of His soul-cleans-ing grace, Un-der the cross,
3. If you need com-fort and faith to go on, Un-der the cross,

un-der the cross; There the poor wan-d'rer is hap-py and blest,
un-der the cross, There you must kneel and look up in His face,
un-der the cross, There the great bat-tle of life can be won,

CHORUS

Un-der the cross of Cal - va - ry. Un-der the cross where my

Sav - ior died, Close I will stay by His wound-ed side, For-ev-er-

more there to a - bide, Un-der the cross of Cal - va - ry.

162 THERE'S A GREAT DAY COMING

BY PERMISSION OF W. L. THOMPSON & CO., EAST LIVERPOOL, OHIO

W. L. Thompson

W. L. Thompson

1. There's a great day com-ing, A great day com-ing, There's a great day com-ing by and by, When the saints and the sin-ners shall be part-ed right and left, Are you read-y for that day to come?

2. There's a bright day com-ing, A bright day com-ing, There's a bright day com-ing by and by, But its bright-ness shall on-ly come to them that love the Lord, Are you read-y for that day to come?

3. There's a sad day com-ing, A sad day com-ing, There's a sad day com-ing by and by, When the sin-ner shall hear his doom, "De-part, I know ye not!" Are you read-y for that day to come?

CHORUS

Are you read-y? Are you read-y? Are you read-y for the judgment day? Are you read-y? Are you read-y for the judgment day?

163 'NEATH THE OLD OLIVE TREES

B. B. McKinney
Duet. Slowly.

B. B. McKinney

1. 'Neath the stars of the night, Walked the Savior of light, In the gar-den of
2. All the sin of the world On the Sav-ior was hurled, As He knelt in the
3. May my song ev-er be Of the love proffered me, By my Lord all a-

dew-lad-ened breeze; Where no light could be found, Je-sus knelt on the ground,
gar-den a-lone; Hear His soul-burdened plea, Let this cup pass from me,
lone on His knees: Praise His won-der-ful name, He who bore all my blame,

CHORUS.

There He prayed 'neath the old ol-ive trees.
"E - ven so, not my will, Thine be done." Neath the old ol-ive trees, 'Neath the
As He knelt 'neath the old ol-ive trees.'

old ol-ive trees, Went the Sav-ior a-lone on His knees, "Not my will, Thine be

done," cried the Father's own Son, As He knelt 'neath the old ol-ive trees.

164 OUR SHEPHERD TRUE

W. C. Martin

D. B. Towner

1. Je - sus leads us like a shep-herd, Dai - ly in - to pas-tures new;
2. Rug-ged seems the road be - fore us, But our Shep-herd leads the way;
3. Mer - cy, grace and peace have found us, And we trust Him more and more;

Je - sus leads us like a shep-herd, Ev - er faith - ful, ev - er true;
He is faith - ful to re-store us When we fal - ter, when we stray;
Sun - lit are the fields a - round us, But the best is on be - fore;

And He guards us in the way, Keeps a vig - il lest we stray, Drives all
Where the sweet-est pasture grows, Where the liv-ing wa - ter flows, Christ, our
Tho' be - yond us lies the gloom Of the val - ley, there is room For the

ad lib.

Chorus

en - e-mies a-way,—Je-sus, Shepherd true! O our Shep - - herd ev - er
Sav-ior, always knows,—He's our Shepherd true!
sun-light in the tomb, With our Sav-ior true! O our Shepherd ever leads us, yes, our

leads us Where the south - wind soft - ly blows, Where the
Shepherd ev-er leads us Where the south-wind soft-ly blows, where the south-wind softly blows,

OUR SHEPHERD TRUE

ad lib.

sweetest pasture grows, Where the living water flows,—Jesus, Shepherd true!

165   CRUCIFIED WITH CHRIST

COPYRIGHT, 1927, BY ROBERT HARKNESS
INTERNATIONAL COPYRIGHT SECURED

Gal. 2: 20

Robert Harkness

I am cru-ci-fied with Christ, I am cru-ci-fied with Christ, Nev-er-the-

less I live, nev-er-the-less I live, Yet not I, but Christ liv-eth in me;

And the life which I now live in the flesh, I live by the faith of the

Son of God, Who loved me, who loved me, and gave Him-self for me.

166 CITY OF GOLD

L. D. Santee

H. L. Brooks

1. There's a beau-ti-ful cit-y that lies far a-way From the
2. From the shad-ows are lift-ed our sor-row-ful eyes, To the
3. And there all of our sor-rows shall fade as a dream As we

earth with its bur-den of tears, Where the night nev-er en-ters but
hills where the an-gels have trod, And our hearts ev-er yearn for our
en-ter the coun-try of rest, While be-fore us in heav-en-ly

shad-ow-less day Shines on thro' e-ter-ni-ty's years.
home in the skies, Our home in the gar-den of God.
beau-ty shall gleam The Man-sions pre-pared for the blest.

CHORUS *Melody in 2d Tenor. Parts hum if desired*

O beau-ti-ful cit-y, Cit - y of gold;
Beau-ti-ful cit-y of gold, of pure gold;

O beau-ti-ful cit-y, Treas-ures un-told;

CITY OF GOLD

O beau-ti-ful cit-y, Cit - - - y of gold; . . .
Beau-ti-ful cit-y of gold, of pure gold;

When shall I rest in that beau-ti-ful cit-y of gold? . . .
rest in that cit-y of gold?

167   OUR HEARTS TURN TO THEE

COPYRIGHT, 1908, BY THE PRAISE PUB. CO.
HOMER A. RODEHEAVER, OWNER

Lizzie DeArmond

With expression

W. A. Post

1. When morning's gold doth shine Bright o - ver land and sea, Our hearts with
2. Dwell in our souls to - day; Make for thy - self a throne, May we in
3. O Fa - ther, kind and true, Guide us from day to day, May we thro'

mf

glad thanks-giv-ing Turn un - to Thee; Thy word un-seals the night,
full sur-ren - der Serve Thee a - lone; Now on Thy al - tar fair,
storm or sun-shine Walk in Thy way; Help us Thy will to know,

rall. e dim.   *p*

Fills earth with heaven's light, Thou art our all in all, On Thee we call.
Lay we each fond de-sire, O may Thy grace di-vine New love in-spire.
More like the Christ to grow, Thine would we ev-er be; We turn to Thee.

168 I AM HAPPY IN HIM

E. O. Excell

E. O. Excell

1. My soul is so hap-py in Je - sus, For He is so precious to me;
2. He sought me so long ere I knew Him, When wand'ring afar from the fold;
3. His love and His mercy sur-round me, His grace like a riv-er doth flow;
4. They say I shall some day be like Him, My cross and my burden lay down;

His voice it is mu-sic to hear it, His face it is heav-en to see.
Safe home in His arms He hath bro't me, To where there are pleasures untold.
His Spir - it, to guide and to com-fort, Is with me wher-ev-er I go.
Till then I will ev - er be faith-ful, In gath - er-ing gems for His crown.

CHORUS.

I am hap-py in Him, ... I am hap-py in Him; .... My
I ...... am hap-py in Him, I ...... am hap-py in Him;

soul with delight He fills day and night, For I am hap-py in Him. A - MEN.

169 ONLY IN JESUS

Jennie Ree

Arr. from Rubinstein
with Chorus by C. H. G.

1. On - ly in Je - sus my heart is at rest; On - ly in Him can my
2. On - ly in Je - sus for-give - ness is found; Grace that in tri - als much
3. On - ly in Je - sus sal - va - tion is mine; Light that for guidance will

spir - it be blest; On - ly on Him ev - 'ry bur - den I roll;
more shall a - bound; Peace a - mid con - flict and joy a - mid pain,
stead - i - ly shine; Pow'r for His serv - ice, His word to o - bey,

CHORUS *Faster*

He is the foun - tain of life to my soul.
Turn - ing earth loss - es to heav - en - ly gain. On - ly in Je - sus
Strength that for - ev - er shall be as my stay.

my hope shall be, In life and in e - ter - ni - ty; On - ly in

Je - sus would I a - bide, Till in His pres - ence I'm sat - is - fied.

THE YIELDED HOUR

170

Rev. Samuel McP. Glasgow

Jesse B. Thomas

1. When my will is bend-ed low, When His will for me I know, When the
heart is read-y in the yield-ed hour; There's a peace I nev-er knew,
There is strength and courage, too, There's a com-ing of the Ho-ly Spir-it's pow'r.

2. "Lord, what wilt Thou have me do? To Thy will I would be true," Is the
heart-cry spo-ken in the yield-ed hour. Then His call will clear-ly sound,
Then His guide-posts will be found, With the call will come the Ho-ly Spir-it's pow'r.

3. There's a noonday brightness ours, There's a flood of might-y pow'rs, And a
heav'n-ly vi-sion in the yield-ed hour; There's His fel-low-ship di-vine,
Joy of the re-deemed is mine, Home for-ev-er by the Ho-ly Spir-it's pow'r.

CHORUS

O the pow'r, . . . the pow'r of God! How it surg-es thro' the
O the pow'r, the pow'r of God!

soul that's o-pen wide! O the peace, . . . the peace of
o-pen wide! O the peace,

THE YIELDED HOUR

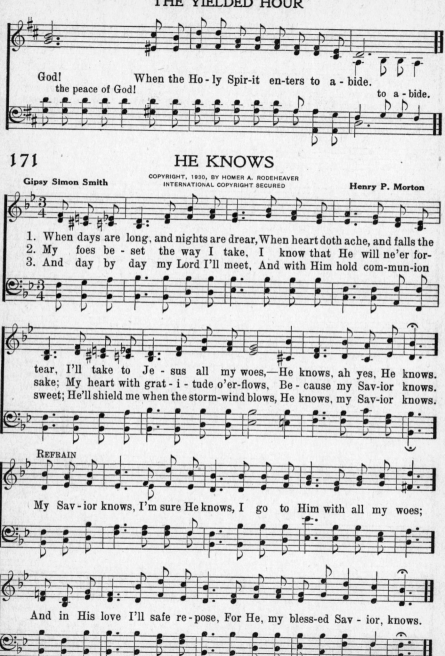

God! When the Ho-ly Spir-it en-ters to a-bide.

the peace of God! to a-bide.

171   HE KNOWS

Gipsy Simon Smith   Henry P. Morton

1. When days are long, and nights are drear, When heart doth ache, and falls the
2. My foes be-set the way I take, I know that He will ne'er for-
3. And day by day my Lord I'll meet, And with Him hold com-mun-ion

tear, I'll take to Je-sus all my woes,—He knows, ah yes, He knows.
sake; My heart with grat-i-tude o'er-flows, Be-cause my Sav-ior knows.
sweet; He'll shield me when the storm-wind blows, He knows, my Sav-ior knows.

REFRAIN

My Sav-ior knows, I'm sure He knows, I go to Him with all my woes;

And in His love I'll safe re-pose, For He, my bless-ed Sav-ior, knows.

172 LEAVE IT THERE

Words and Music by C. Albert Tindley   Arr. by Chas. A. Tindley, Jr.

Moderato.

1. If the world from you withhold, of its sil-ver and its gold, And you
2. If your bod-y suf-fers pain, and your health you can't re-gain, And your
3. When your en-e-mies as-sail, and your heart be-gins to fail, Don't for-
4. When your youthful days are gone, and old age is steal-ing on, And your

have to get a-long with mea-ger fare, Just re-mem-ber, from on high He will
soul is al-most sink-ing in de-spair, Je-sus knows the pain you feel, He can
get that God in heav-en an-swers prayer; He will make a way for you and will
bod-y bends be-neath the weight of care, He will nev-er leave you then, He'll go

ev-'ry need sup-ply; Take your bur-den to the Lord and leave it there.
save and He can heal; Take your bur-den to the Lord and leave it there.
lead you safe-ly thro'; Take your bur-den to the Lord and leave it there.
with you to the end; Take your bur-den to the Lord and leave it there.

CHORUS.

Leave it there,...... leave it there,...... Take your bur-den to the
Leave it there,   leave it there,

Lord and leave it there;...... If you trust and nev-er doubt, He will
leave it there;

LEAVE IT THERE

Sure - ly bring you out; Take your burden to the Lord and leave it there.

leave it there.

173   SINCE JESUS CAME

Frederick W. Suffield   COPYRIGHT, 1930, BY MRS. F. W. SUFFIELD   Mrs. F. W. Suffield

DUET. *Alto and Tenor*

1. I once was far a - way and lost, But Je - sus came, But Je - sus
2. I cried to Him in my dis - tress, Then Je - sus came, Then Je - sus
3. I found with - in a hid - den foe, But Je - sus came, But Je - sus
4. I go re - joic - ing on my way, Since Je - sus came, Since Je - sus

came; He bro't me back at such a cost, When Jesus came, When Jesus came.
came; He gave me joy and peace and rest, When Jesus came, When Jesus came.
came; The car - nal mind then had to go, When Jesus came, When Jesus came.
came; My path grows brighter day by day, Since Jesus came, Since Jesus came.

REFRAIN

Je - sus came new life to give, Je - sus died that I might live; Life a-

bun - dant I've re - ceived Since Je - sus came, Since Je - sus came.

NOTHING SATISFIES BUT JESUS

Mrs. C. H. Morris

Mrs. C. H. Morris

1. Noth-ing sat-is-fies but Je - sus, Bread of life to mor-tals giv'n;
2. Since I heard the voice of Je - sus, Since mine eyes be-held the King,
3. With His joy my heart is thrill-ing, All my hope in Him I see;

May His pres-ence now re - fresh us Like the morn-ing dew from Heav'n!
All my love, my heart's af - fec - tion, All I have, to Him I bring.
Doubt, and gloom, and fear dis - pel - ling, Christ is All in all to me.

CHORUS.

Give me Je - sus, give me Je - sus, Take the world, but give me Je - sus,
Give me Je-sus, give me Je-sus,

To sat - is - fy . . with ev-'ry blessing, His love and peace my soul pos-sess-ing;

To all be-side, my heart re-plies: There's naught but Jesus sat-is-fies! A - MEN.

175 WHEN THE SHADOWS FLEE AWAY

Robert Harkness

Robert Harkness

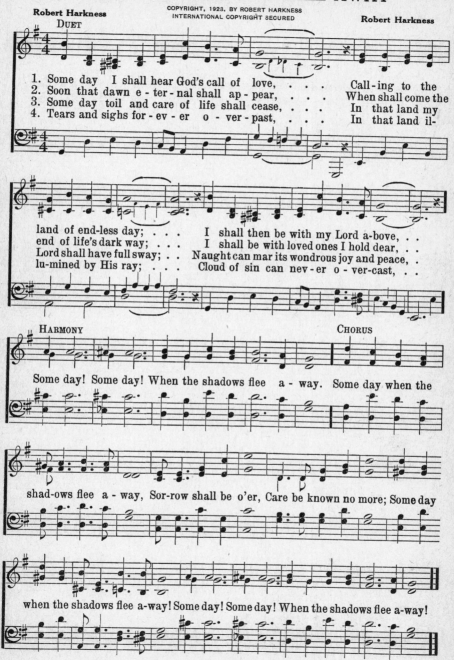

DUET

1. Some day I shall hear God's call of love, ... Call-ing to the
2. Soon that dawn e-ter-nal shall ap-pear, ... When shall come the
3. Some day toil and care of life shall cease, ... In that land my
4. Tears and sighs for-ev-er o-ver-past, ... In that land il-

land of end-less day; ... I shall then be with my Lord a-bove, ..
end of life's dark way; ... I shall be with loved ones I hold dear, ..
Lord shall have full sway; .. Naught can mar its wondrous joy and peace, ..
lu-mined by His ray; ... Cloud of sin can nev-er o-ver-cast, ..

HARMONY   CHORUS

Some day! Some day! When the shadows flee a-way. Some day when the

shad-ows flee a-way, Sor-row shall be o'er, Care be known no more; Some day

when the shadows flee a-way! Some day! Some day! When the shadows flee a-way!

WHY CHRIST DIED

Robert Harkness

Robert Harkness

SOLO

1. I well re-mem-ber how Christ died for me On yon-der Cross—
2. Free-ly He of-fered His grace to be-stow; He died for you—
3. Will you not trust Him, O sin-la-den soul? He died for you—

On yon-der Cross; He suf-fered an-guish on Cal-va-ry,
He died for you; Tho' all un-wor-thy His love to know,
He died for you; Come with sin's bur-den, Christ can make whole,

Bought my free par-don, gave lib-er-ty. Yes! I re-mem-ber how
O how He loved you, dy-ing in woe: Yes! I re-mem-ber how
On-ly be-lieve Him, make Him your goal. Yes! I re-mem-ber how

Christ died for me On yon-der Cross— on yon-der Cross.
Christ died for you On yon-der Cross— on yon-der Cross.
Christ died for you On yon-der Cross— on yon-der Cross.

177 CARRY ME BACK

COPYRIGHT, 1928, BY THORO HARRIS

James Bland

1. Car-ry me back to Cal-v'ry's mountain: There's where my Savior died for
2. Car-ry me back to Cal-v'ry's mountain, There let me live in the

CHO.—*Car-ry me back to Cal-v'ry's mountain Where Je-sus died my re-*

me up-on the tree, There's where He speaks to my spirit so sweet-ly; No oth-er
shadow of His cross, Kin-dling my love in the love there uncovered; There let me

bellious heart to win; There let me bathe in the pure cleansing fountain, Flowing to

place could be half so dear to me. Long time I wandered a-way from my Savior,
weep till I lose my worthless dross. O, there my spir-it is touched by His goodness,

save me and keep me from all sin.

Day aft-er day by my bur-den sore op-prest; There, 'neath His cross, Je-sus
There Jesus speaks out of flow-ing wounds to me; And when at last I am

gave me His par-don, Lift-ing my bur-den, He bro't me in-to rest.
safe home in heav-en, E'en there I'll thrill to the tho't of Cal-va-ry.

D. C. Chorus.

180 CRUCIFY! CRUCIFY!

MUSIC AND ARRANGEMENT OF WORDS COPYRIGHT, 1925, BY W. E. M. HACKLEMAN
STANDARD PUB. CO., OWNER

William Dunroy Reed

W. E. M. Hackleman

1. Christ is walking thro' the streets, Looking in each face He meets, *Ten - der-*
2. Christ is walking thro' the shops, By each workman there He stops, *Anx - ious-*
3. Christ is walking thro' the homes, "Guest of hon-or" there, He comes, *Gra - cious-*
4. Christ is walking thro' the slums, With His cross and crown He comes, *Plead - ing-*
5. Christ is walking ev - 'ry-where, With His heart bowed low with care, *Yearn-ing-*

ly! Not a - lone in Church He stands, Where suppl'ants kneel with folded hands,
ly! He would lift the heav-y load; He would re-move the thorn-y road;
ly! Speaking words of love and cheer; Blessings He gives the children dear;
ly! Stand-ing in the dens of shame, Calls He the wand'ring ones by name:
ly! But the peo - ple lift their eyes, With longing hearts toward the skies;

CRUCIFY! CRUCIFY!

But in the bus-y walks of life, A-mid the tu-mult and the strife:
Smooth ev-'ry wrin-kle from the brow; Wounds He would heal and none allow:
Sweet peace He brings the broken heart, "I, from thee, nev-er will de-part:"
His heart o'er-flow-ing with God's love, Bids He each sin-ner look a-bove:
They knowing not that near them stands Christ off'ring rest with outstretched hands:

mf *f*

8va.

REFRAIN

mf

Walks He where the peo-ple meet; Walks He there with

bleed-ing feet; But they scorn Him, pass Him by, And in their

ff *rit.* *ac-cel-*

fff *fff*

mad-ness loud-ly cry— Cru-ci-fy! Cru-ci-fy!

-e-ran-do cres.

fff *fff*

181 WHEN I TAKE MY VACATION IN HEAVEN

(This title was suggested by Katherine Perkins, age 11, at Huntington Beach, Calif.)
Dedicated to the friends of the Huntington Beach, Calif., Tent Meeting, June–July, 1925

Words and Melody by Herbert Buffum   Harmony by R. E. Winsett

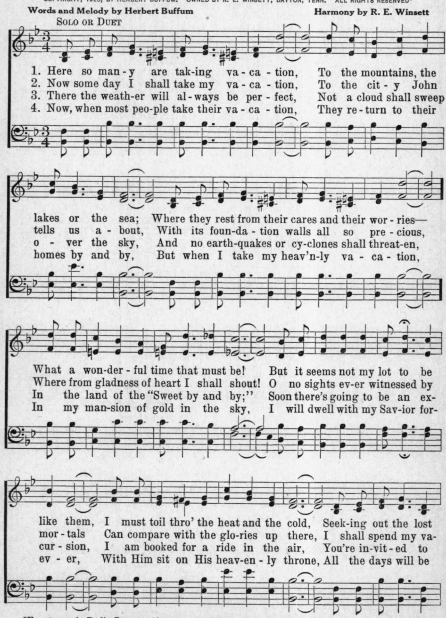

1. Here so man-y are tak-ing va - ca - tion, To the mountains, the lakes or the sea; Where they rest from their cares and their wor - ries— What a won-der - ful time that must be! But it seems not my lot to be like them, I must toil thro' the heat and the cold, Seek-ing out the lost

2. Now some day I shall take my va - ca - tion, To the cit - y John tells us a - bout, With its foun-da - tion walls all so pre - cious, Where from gladness of heart I shall shout! O no sights ev-er witnessed by mor - tals Can compare with the glo-ries up there, I shall spend my va-

3. There the weath-er will al-ways be per - fect, Not a cloud shall sweep o - ver the sky, And no earth-quakes or cy-clones shall threat-en, In the land of the "Sweet by and by;" Soon there's going to be an ex-cur - sion, I am booked for a ride in the air, You're in-vit - ed to

4. Now, when most peo-ple take their va - ca - tion, They re-turn to their homes by and by, But when I take my heav'n-ly va - ca - tion, In my man-sion of gold in the sky, I will dwell with my Sav-ior for-ev - er, With Him sit on His heav-en - ly throne, All the days will be

WHEN I TAKE MY VACATION IN HEAVEN

sheep on the moun-tains, Bring-ing wan-der-ers back to the fold.
ca - tion with Je - sus, In the place He went on to pre - pare.
share my va - ca - tion, And the feast with our Bride-groom to share.
one long va - ca - tion When my Sav-ior takes me to His home.

CHORUS

When I take my va - ca-tion in heav-en, What a won-der-ful time that will be!

Hearing concerts by the heav-en-ly cho-rus, And the face of my Sav-ior I'll see.

Sitting down on the banks of the riv-er, 'Neath the shade of the ev-er-green tree,

I shall rest from my burdens for-ev-er—Won't you spend your vacation with me?

This song can be had in octavo form, 15 cents, from R. E. Winsett, Dayton, Tenn.

182 I WONDER HOW THE OLD FOLKS ARE AT HOME

Herbert S. Lambert   F. W. Vandersloot

SOLO. *Andante moderato*

1. 'Tis not so man-y years a-go, when as a boy I played A-
2. This world grows wea-ry day by day, I'm lone-ly and I'm sad, I

mid the scenes so dear to me, from morn till evening shade; No place so dear to
long a-gain to see the scenes I knew when but a lad; To play with lit-tle

child-hood days as my old coun-try home, Un-til one day I said "Good-by," and
broth-er as we whiled the hours away, No tho't had we of sor-row then, our

faster

went a - way to roam. The old folks said, "God bless you, boy, and may you soon re-
hearts were light and gay. I see a-gain the old school-house, the church up-on the

tempo I

turn; Two brok-en hearts a-wait you here, two souls will watch and yearn." The
hill, The lane that leads to Grandma's house is fresh in mem -'ry still; A

I WONDER HOW THE OLD FOLKS ARE AT HOME

years have come and gone away, no news from son at home, No lov-ing mes-sage
wand'ring boy a-lone tonight, with tho'ts of home, sweet home, Still wonders how the

rit. CHORUS *slowly*

to the boy who went a-way to roam. I won-der how the old folks are at
old folks are, this boy who went to roam. hear the cat-tle low-ing in the

home; I won-der if they miss me while I roam; I won-der if they pray
lane, And see a-gain the fields of golden grain; I al-most hear them sigh

1
for the boy that went a-way And left his kind old parents all a - lone; I

2 *rit.*
as they bade their boy "Good-by;" I wonder how they are at home, sweet home.

The above song published complete in sheet music, solo piano waltzes, band, full orchestra, etc. by
Vandersloot Music Pub. Co. Williamsport, Pa.

IF I WERE A VOICE

From "Song Crown"

Isaac Beverly Woodbury

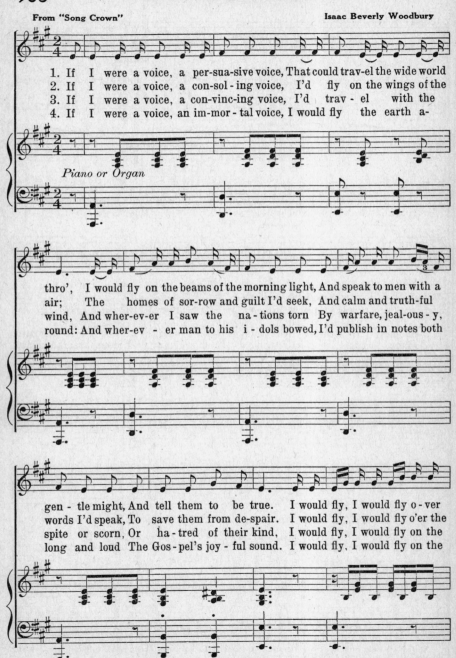

1. If I were a voice, a per-sua-sive voice, That could trav-el the wide world
2. If I were a voice, a con-sol-ing voice, I'd fly on the wings of the
3. If I were a voice, a con-vinc-ing voice, I'd trav-el with the
4. If I were a voice, an im-mor-tal voice, I would fly the earth a-

Piano or Organ

thro', I would fly on the beams of the morning light, And speak to men with a
air; The homes of sor-row and guilt I'd seek, And calm and truth-ful
wind, And wher-ev-er I saw the na-tions torn By warfare, jeal-ous-y,
round: And wher-ev-er man to his i-dols bowed, I'd publish in notes both

gen-tle might, And tell them to be true. I would fly, I would fly o-ver
words I'd speak, To save them from de-spair. I would fly, I would fly o'er the
spite or scorn, Or ha-tred of their kind, I would fly, I would fly on the
long and loud The Gos-pel's joy-ful sound. I would fly, I would fly on the

IF I WERE A VOICE

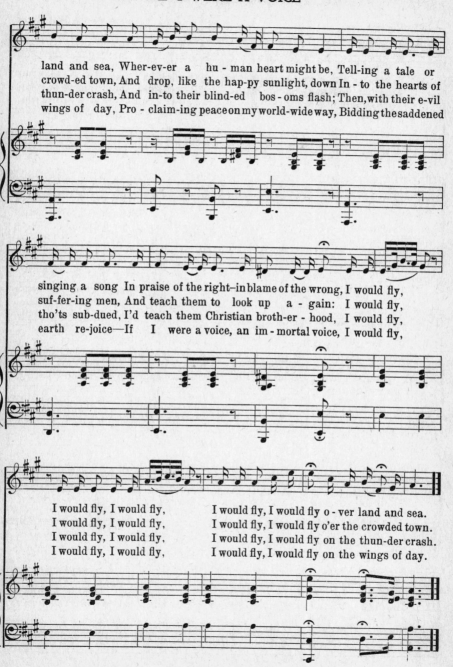

land and sea, Wher-ev-er a hu - man heart might be, Tell-ing a tale or
crowd-ed town, And drop, like the hap-py sunlight, down In - to the hearts of
thun-der crash, And in-to their blind-ed bos - oms flash; Then, with their e-vil
wings of day, Pro - claim-ing peace on my world-wide way, Bidding the saddened

singing a song In praise of the right—in blame of the wrong, I would fly,
suf-fer-ing men, And teach them to look up a - gain: I would fly,
tho'ts sub-dued, I'd teach them Christian broth-er - hood, I would fly,
earth re-joice—If I were a voice, an im - mortal voice, I would fly,

I would fly, I would fly,   I would fly, I would fly o - ver land and sea.
I would fly, I would fly,   I would fly, I would fly o'er the crowded town.
I would fly, I would fly,   I would fly, I would fly on the thun-der crash.
I would fly, I would fly,   I would fly, I would fly on the wings of day.

SOME DAY, IT WON'T BE LONG

L. B. Bridgers

L. B. Bridgers

1. Some day I'll cross the mys-tic stream, It won't be long, it may be soon;
2. Some day this mor - tal life shall cease, It won't be long, it may be soon;
3. He's com-ing back with glo-ry rare, It won't be long, it may be soon;
4. Then as you trav - el on life's way, Thro' waters deep, or bil-lows' foam;

Some day I'll lay my bur-dens down, It won't be long, it may be soon;
Some day I'll see my Sav-ior's face, It won't be long, it may be soon;
We'll rise to meet Him in the air, It won't be long, it may be soon;
You may have Je - sus as your stay, He'll walk with you and lead you home.

Some day I'll reach the gold-en shore, And dwell with Je - sus ev - er - more,
Some day I'll leave this vale of tears, For - get the strug-gles of long years,
If   He should call me, this I know: I'm saved and read-y now to go,
O broth - er, will you let Him in? He'll save and keep you free from sin,

I'll meet the ones who've gone be-fore, It won't be long, it may be soon.
I'll know no sor - row, pain, nor fears; It won't be long, it may be soon.
I'm wait-ing with my heart a - glow; It won't be long, it may be soon.
Till heav-en's door you en - ter in; It won't be long, it may be soon.

℆ *Sing after last verse.* FINE.

D. S.

D. S.—There'll be no sorrow there. There'll be no sorrow there, In heav'n above, where all is love,

INDEX

Titles in light face type are SOLOS. Titles in black face type are DUETS, some of which, however, may also be used as SOLOS.

TOPICAL INDEX

IT IS DIFFERENT NOW!

T. O. Chisholm   B. D. Ackley

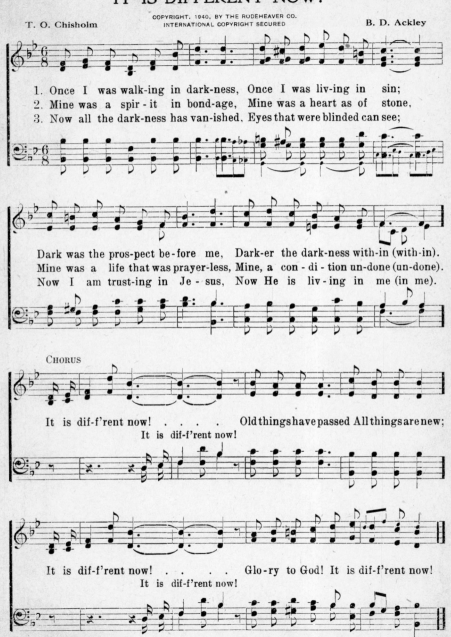

1. Once I was walk-ing in dark-ness, Once I was liv-ing in sin;
2. Mine was a spir-it in bond-age, Mine was a heart as of stone,
3. Now all the dark-ness has van-ished, Eyes that were blinded can see;

Dark was the pros-pect be-fore me, Dark-er the dark-ness with-in (with-in).
Mine was a life that was prayer-less, Mine, a con-di-tion un-done (un-done).
Now I am trust-ing in Je-sus, Now He is liv-ing in me (in me).

CHORUS

It is dif-f'rent now! . . . . Old things have passed All things are new;
It is dif-f'rent now!

It is dif-f'rent now! . . . . Glo-ry to God! It is dif-f'rent now!
It is dif-f'rent now!

(Written for and dedicated to Mel Trotter in honor of the 40th anniversary of the City Rescue Mission, January 14-21, 1940. B. D. A.)